The Art of Invention

The Art of Invention

Patent Models
and Their Makers

William and Marlys Ray

Foreword by Peter Goldmark

The Pyne Press
Princeton

Left, Improved Steam Radiator, Charles A. Wilson, Cincinnati, Ohio, July 26, 1859, Patent No. 24,897.

SOUTH HALL, MUSEUM OF MODELS, PATENT OFFICE.

Contents

Foreword

The significance of *The Art of Invention* transcends the ingenious devices, the fascinating text, and the magnificent illustrations it presents to the reader. It is a book which places us at the threshold of a period which was probably more critical to the development of Western civilization than any other since the beginning of recorded history. And it offers a unique historical perspective on the gadget-filled age in which we live today.

Not until man's most far-reaching invention, the movable-type printing press, was introduced in the middle of the fifteenth century, did everyday life undergo changes to any extent. The full impact of Johann Gutenberg's invention was not realized for several centuries, but gradually communication through the printed word transformed teaching and learning into a universal process. From this time on, the world around us began to change at an ever increasing rate.

As a result of the interchange of printed information, scientists and inventors no longer had to spend a lifetime creating what someone else might already have discovered. Therefore, research and invention, during the next several centuries, could be built on work done by others, and become more and more systematic and need-oriented.

During the nineteenth century, science and technology grew at an ever increasing rate, a direct effect of the endless stream of theories and ideas unleashed from the minds of thousands of highly stimulated scientists and inventors. As *The Art of Invention* so clearly illustrates, in the last century virtually everything could be invented or discovered. For that reason, ingenious individuals were able to create new devices and theories to fit their own talents, training, and the resources which they had at their disposal.

Today, new processes, theories and inventions are created at a much greater cost in money, manpower and time. We are scraping the bottom of the barrel. The blessings which science and technology have achieved within a brief moment of human history are, as we look back, of a mixed variety. Men everywhere are finding it increasingly difficult to adapt to the still increasing rate of change and, therefore, it has become more and more urgent that we redirect our scientific and inventive resources so that all men can truly enjoy the fruits of creative endeavor. *The Art of Invention* captures most perfectly that timeless inventive and searching spirit of men which can be stimulated to serve mankind as well today as it has in past centuries.

Peter Goldmark

Preface

The Art of Invention is intended to be a tribute to the ingenuity and imaginative spirit of the nineteenth-century American inventor. These qualities are most evident in the patent models submitted to the United States Patent Office along with the patent application.

The models were required by law until the 1880's as an aid to the patent examiner in determining the originality of an invention. A majority of these miniature objects were still-born; they saw no more than the dusty shelves of the Patent Office. Those illustrated in this book have been chosen for their aesthetic rather than historic merit, resulting in a collection which includes some significant inventions by famous individuals, but is predominantly evidence of the inventiveness of the obscure dreamer whose visions of wealth and fame were predicated on and nurtured by such success stories as those of Fulton, Colt and McCormick.

Manuals for the inventor were abundant throughout the century, and were replete with avuncular advice about the necessity of submitting a proper model to the Patent Office. This model might also be useful in attracting the interest of a manufacturer and/or investor. Under no condition, the refrain went, should an inventor appear poor or desperate in the eyes of a manufacturer who was very ready to buy up the patent rights for the proverbial song.

With few exceptions, every major invention has had a prototype in an earlier century, but it was in the nineteenth century that every major source of power was developed to enable the seemingly wildest dreams to be realized. Today, with corporations employing full-time research teams to advance technology, the lone tinkerer or mechanic, as inventor, has faded from view. And with the disappearance of this enterprising figure, we have lost much of the drama and the color of the art of invention. His spirit and hopes, however, can be seen in his patent models, courageous and charming, at times beautiful and/or absurd. They are vibrant evidence of his solitary search for an improved way of life.

We wish to acknowledge with special thanks the kind assistance of the Assistant Director of the Museum of History and Technology of the Smithsonian Institute, Silvio A. Bedini, and the following members of the Smithsonian staff: Richard Ahlborn, Don Berkebile, Robert Billingsly, Herbert Collins, Grace Cooper, Warren Danzenbaker, Craddock Goins, Jr., Irwin Goodwin, Dr. Elizabeth Harris, John Hoffmann, Everett Jackson, James Knowles, Jr., Dr. Uta Merzbach, Danny Morris, Eugene Ostroff, Terry Sharrer, Winthrop Shaw of the Air and Space Museum, Elliot Sivowitch, John Stein, Robert Vogel and John White.

Our thanks are due also to Mr. and Mrs. O. Rundle Gilbert and Mr. and Mrs. Robert Gilbert, for their amiable cooperation; and to Isaac Fleischmann and Oscar Mastin of the United States Patent Office; James Polaskus and Joseph B. Howerton of the United States National Archives; Milton Kaplan of the Library of Congress; Robert A. Truax, Librarian, The Columbia Historical Society; Joanne Hohler, State Historical Society of Wisconsin; Henry E. Edmunds, Director, Ford Archives, Greenfield Village; Robert Koolakian, Curator, Edison Institute, Greenfield Village; Peter Cousins, Curator, Department of Agriculture, Greenfield Village; Dr. Walter Heacock, General Director, and Robert Howard, Curator, Eleutherian Mills-Hagley Foundation; Richmond Williams, Director, Eleutherian Mills Historical Library.

Catherine T. Engel, The State Historical Society of Colorado; Jane Alderfer, Chicago Historical Society; Kenneth Roberts, Kenneth Roberts Publishing Co.; James T. Hickey, Curator, Lincoln Collection, Illinois State Historical Library; Sharon Ealius, Transportation Library, University of Michigan; George M. White, Architect of the Capitol; Mrs. Florian H. Thayn, Head, Art and Reference Library, Office of the Architect of the Capitol; Patrick Symes, Patents Collection, New York Public Library; John Chropovka, Science Division, New York Public Library; Elizabeth Roth and Roberta Wong, Prints Collection, New York Public Library; Blair Noback and Thomas E. Hayes, President, D. Ballauf Manufacturing Co.

The Art of Invention

The United States Patent Office as seen in 1847.

I. Patent Pending

The model, not more than twelve inches square, should be neatly made, the name of the inventor should be printed or engraved upon, or affixed to it, in a durable manner. Models forwarded without a name are disregarded by the commissioner; and are not entered on record, and therefore liable to be lost or mislaid.
—Patent Act of July 4, 1836

Sixty years after the founding of the Republic, the American system for securing patent protection was in shambles. Senator John Ruggles of Maine had reported earlier in the year, "Frauds develop, people copy existing patents, make slight changes and are granted patents. Patents have become of little value and the object of the patent laws is in great measure defeated." This had not been the intention of those who had carefully formulated the regulations for obtaining such security in April of 1790. At that time it was stipulated that the applicant should submit a specification sheet, drawing and model to a board of commissioners. Within a short period of time, however, the mechanics, artisans, scientists and just plain tinkerers of the young nation had proved that they were an ingenious, if not unruly, lot. Yet, not even that most inventive figure, Thomas Jefferson, could have foreseen the need for more than a board of part-time examiners, a few rooms to hold the patent models that would eventually number in the hundreds of thousands.

When the delegates to the Constitutional Convention met in Philadelphia in 1787, the patent issue was both important and sensitive. The colonists had a natural aversion to the monopolies granted as favors by European monarchs, and everyone present agreed in principle to the granting of limited monopolies in the form of patents. James Madison and Charles Pinckney submitted proposals concerning such protection, and on September 5th the clause on patents and copyrights was adopted. The Constitution was signed on September 17th with the provision in Article 1, Section 8, that "Congress shall have the power . . . to promote the progress of science and useful arts, by securing for limited times to authors and inventors the exclusive right to their respective writings and discoveries."

When President Washington addressed Congress on January 8, 1790, he urged "effectual encouragement to the exertion of skill and genius at home," and a patent bill was submitted and passed on February 16th. The first Patent Commission, members of which assumed the title of Commissioners for the Promotion of Useful Arts, included Thomas Jefferson, Secretary of State, Henry Knox, Secretary of War, and the Attorney General, Edmund Randolph. They could grant a fourteen-year patent.

As a patent examiner, one can assume that Jefferson personally approved all the applications. His own inventions are well known: the swivel chair, a pedometer, a shooting stick, a hemp-treating machine, and, perhaps most important, an improvement in the mold board of the plow, which earned him a decoration from the French Institute. The first U. S. patent was granted in 1790 to Samuel Hopkins of Pittsford, Vermont, for an improvement in the "making of Pot Ash and Pearl Ash by a new Apparatus and Process," and 54 other patents were issued in that and the following two years.

Jefferson, the politician, wasn't able, however, to successfully oppose the Patent Bill of 1793 which abolished the examination system. It was replaced by a simple registration procedure, meaning that anyone who applied, and paid a thirty dollar fee, was granted a patent. The importance of a patent was lost in the clerical function of collecting revenue. The inventor was not responsible for novelty or usefulness in his invention, nor was he required to furnish drawings or a model. The Commission was abolished and the Secretary of State was made responsible for the granting of fourteen-year patents. In the case of two applicants for the same patent at the same time, a situation termed an interference, the Secretary of State chose a board to determine the case.

Edmund Randolph replaced Jefferson as Secretary of State in 1794. The most famous patent granted under his tenure was that for Eli Whitney's cotton gin in March of 1794. Unfortunately for Whitney, there was no way he could protect his claim, nor keep anyone from making their own simply constructed gin of his design. He lost more money and time in litigation than he ever collected in royalties that were his due. Financial success only came later for Whitney when he set up an interchangeable parts for the manufacture of muskets.

When the seat of government moved to Washington in 1800, a Patent Office was temporarily established in the Treasury office. In 1802, with Jefferson in the White House and James Madison as his Secretary of State, it became part of the State Department, and was moved to Blodgett's Hotel, an early wooden structure which was the District's first theater. An intimate friend of all the prominent in Washington, and a neighbor of Madison's, Dr. William Thornton, was appointed the first Patent Chief, or Supervisor, at an annual salary of $1400.

Dr. Thornton was born on the West Indies island of Tortola, where his father was governor. His family was prominent among the Friends in England, and Thornton was sent there to be educated. He studied medicine with the leading doctors of the time in Edinburgh. His main interest, like Jefferson's, was in architecture. Thornton described his first architectural enterprise rather matter of factly: "I saw a publication for a public library in Philadelphia offering a premium for the best ... I got some books and worked a few days, then gave them a plan in the ancient Ionic Order which carried the day." Its foundation was laid August 31, 1789.

In 1793 his plan for the Capitol won the competition, and the final approval of President Washington. Of his prize, Jefferson wrote: "Thornton's plan had captivated the eyes and judgment of all. It is simple, noble, beautiful, excellently arranged, and moderate in size." The country house of James Madison, Montpelier, was one of his designs. He planned the brick mansion, Woodlawn, near Mount Vernon, for George Washington to give to his step-granddaughter, Nellie Custis, as a wedding gift. Perhaps the greatest surviving proof of Thornton's talent is the Octagon, a brick Georgian structure built in 1880 by Colonel John Tayloe, the most distinguished race horse breeder in America at the time.

In 1794 Washington had appointed Thornton one of the Commissioners to supervise the surveys and layouts of the District's streets and squares, approve the locations for government buildings and bridges, and contract the workers for the projects. Since there was a constant shortage of building funds, the Commission also sold city lots for revenue. Thorn-

Dr. William Thornton.

Opposite above, Thornton drawing, East Front, United States Capitol. Although later revised by Benjamin Latrobe, Thornton's plan established the design and character of the building.

Opposite below, Blodgett's Hotel, home of the Patent Office from 1810 until its total devastation by fire in 1836. A Washington landmark, it had never been used as a hotel, but was the first theater in the District.

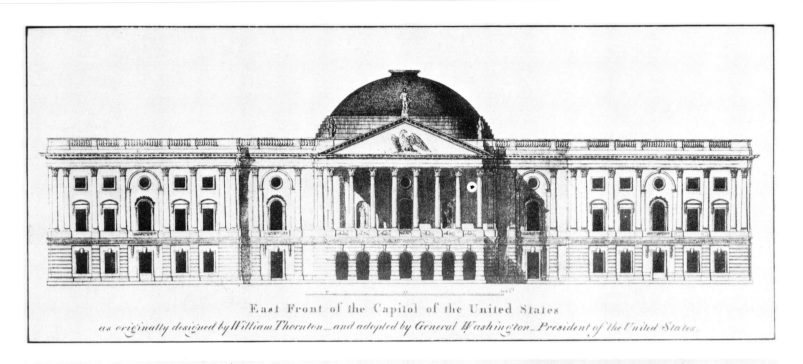

East Front of the Capitol of the United States

as originally designed by William Thornton — and adopted by General Washington — President of the United States.

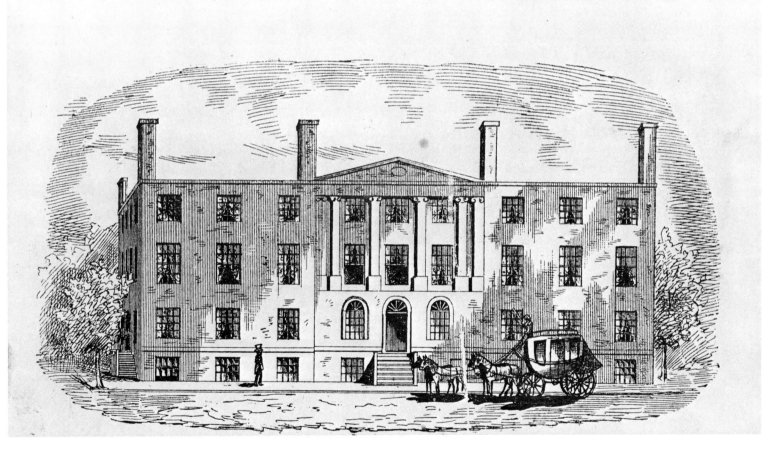

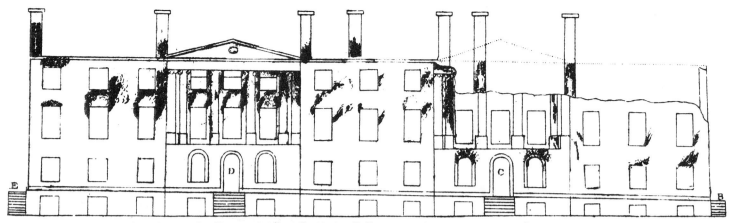

RUINS OF THE POST AND PATENT OFFICES AT WASHINGTON AFTER THE FIRE IN 1836.

ton negotiated loans in Philadelphia and in England to cover construction costs. It is obvious that several men held different and sundry government posts simultaneously while pursuing a private career. Thornton was one of them. In May of 1802 he assumed the new position of Superintendent of Patents, and held this office until his death in 1828. At various periods, he also served as a justice of peace, a commissioner of bankruptcy, and as a member of the Levy Court.

Always a controversial figure, Thornton the Inventor attracted especially harsh criticism in his new position. He held several patents (this was subsequently prohibited of all Patent Office employees), and claimed to have been the first to apply steam to boat propulsion. He was a longtime associate, friend and defender of John Fitch, a luckless inventor who ran a steamboat up the Delaware in 1788. Thornton attempted to withhold popular acclaim from James Fulton as the inventor of the steamboat, and claimed Fulton saw his and Fitch's drawings in his office in 1806. His 1810 pamphlet in defense of Fitch was a brilliant effort to fix Fitch's place in history. All the controversy and criticism surrounding Thornton's activities in the Patent Office could never obscure one of his finest moments, nor detract from the credit that is his and his alone for saving the Patent Office, then in Blodgett's Hotel, from being burned to the ground by the British on August 25, 1814.

According to his own account, he secured all the public papers a few days before, and sent them "to a place of perfect safety, (leaving my own property unattended to) . . . The next day I removed with my family in the retreating army from the City, and beheld in deep regret, that night, the tremendous conflagration of our public buildings, etc. Hearing next morning, while at breakfast in Georgetown, that the British were preparing to burn the War Office and the public building containing the models of the arts, I was desirous not only of saving an instrument that had cost me great labor, but of preserving if possible the building and all the models . . . I therefore left my breakfast and hastened forward."

Thornton's impassioned if exaggerated pleas to the British and fortunate timing resulted in Blodgett's Hotel being the only government building that was spared the torch. He wrote later of his plea to the British major on duty: "I told him that there was nothing but private property of any consequence, and that any public property to which he objected might be burnt in the street, provided the building might be preserved, which contained hundreds of models of the arts, and that it would be impossible to remove them, and to burn what would be useful to all mankind, would be as barbarous as formerly to burn the Alexandrian Library, for which the Turks have been ever since condemned by all enlightened nations."

Four less flamboyant patent commissioners served the Office until 1835, when the young Senator from Maine, John Ruggles began his investigation. The Senator and sometime inventor soon reported, "For more than forty years, the Department of State has passed on every application for patent without any examination of the merit or novelty of the invention. Many of the patents granted are worthless and void. Many are in conflict with one another and a great many lawsuits arise from this condition."

The Patent Act of July 4, 1836 reestablished the examination system of 1790, and the necessity of determining the utility and novelty of an invention. It stipulated a search by Patent Office examiners for any pre-existing patents or inventions. The application, drawing and model were to be submitted, and a fourteen-year patent, with a possible seven-year extension, might be granted. The law stated that the patentee would

NORTH HALL, MUSEUM OF MODELS, PATENT OFFICE.

In the early morning hours of December 15, 1836, Mr. Crown, a messenger for the Post Office, was awakened from a light sleep in the Postmaster's office by the smell of smoke. He called to Mr. Cox, a clerk, asleep in the back room. When they opened their door they were met by black billowing smoke which filled the main room. They could hear the fire crackling, but could see nothing in choking blackness as they felt their way to the door. They ran to the watchman's quarters a short distance away. After arousing the bell-ringer at the church to sound an alarm, they hurried back to save any documents they could. To their dismay, the sleepy bell-ringer couldn't see any flames, so he tolled the bell a few times and went back to bed. It was more than a half hour later, after another frantic rousing, that the alarm bells were finally ringing through the Capital.

By the time the first fire engine arrived and buckets were being passed, flames from the roof filled the sky, only moments after they had burst from the cellar. In an hour the building was devastated, as were its contents. Newspapers chided the government for the "utter absurdity and improvidence of the structures to which the public archives, records, and Government accounts have been hitherto for the most part confided." They noted their good fortune that it was a windless night, and not the hurricane-like spectre that plagued the city just twenty-four hours previous to the holocaust. But everyone agreed that "Of all the amount of loss of papers and property sustained by this disaster, that which is most to be regretted (because irreparable) is that of the whole of the great repository of models of machines in the Patent Office. The smouldering ashes now only remain of that collected evidence of the penetration, ingenuity, and enterprise which peculiarly distinguish the descendants of Europe in the Western World."

Senator Ruggles' report on the fire itemized the loss, including 168 volumes of records, 26 portfolios of approximately 9,000 drawings, the entire library of 230 volumes, and about 7,000 models. Ruggles fondly described many of the important models in several departments. He spoke with deep regret of a volume of Fulton's drawings, "elegantly executed . . . embracing three beautiful representations of his steamer making its first triumphant struggle against the opposing current of the Hudson . . . with a beautiful sketching of the surrounding scenery smiling at the victory which science and art had at last achieved over the power of the winds and the waters . . . ."

He proposed that perhaps 3,000 of the most interesting and important models be replaced, and appealed to the inventors for information needed in the restoration of them and of records. The following year Congress appropriated $100,000 for the reconstruction of the Patent Office's visual history, under the direction of Commissioner Henry L. Ellsworth. Dependent on the patentees and their descendants for this monumental task of duplication, the results were incomplete. Many of the models were reproduced and arrived with new applications at the Old City Hall, the temporary home of the Patent Office until the new building was completed.

"furnish a model of his invention in all cases which admit of a representation by model, of a convenient size to exhibit advantageously its several parts. The model, not more than twelve inches square, should be neatly made, the name of the inventor should be printed or engraved upon, or affixed to it, in a durable manner. Models forwarded without a name are disregarded by the commissioner; and are not entered on record, and are therefore liable to be lost or mislaid."

The application fee for a citizen was still $30, $500 for British subjects, and $300 for any other alien. The head of the Patent Office was to be a commissioner, appointed by the President, subject to the approval of the Senate, and was to receive a salary of $3,000 a year. He was made responsible for all matters concerning patents, had a chief clerk, an examiner, two clerks as draftsmen, a lesser clerk, and a messenger. He was to provide a display for the models in galleries, soon to become a favorite tourist attraction.

With this legislation was initiated the present numbering system, and Senator Ruggles was granted Patent Number 1 for a locomotive steam engine "designed to give a multiplied tractive power to the locomotive and to prevent the evil of the sliding of the wheels." Previously, patents were listed only by the inventor's name, date and title. All was not peaceful, however, in the newly reconstituted Patent Office. Quarters for the staff and the collection of models and drawings were still located in Blodgett's Hotel—awaiting completion of a new building.

For the new building Congress approved the design of William Parker Elliot, who had worked with Dr. Thornton as a mechanical draughtsman in the Patent Office. It was inspired by his early study of the Parthenon, with a portico of sixteen columns, the entablature and pediment all the size and proportion of the Athenian temple. President Jackson also approved, with the condition that the structure be built on one side of the lot on 8th Street, N.W., between F and G Streets, to allow a squatter's log cabin to remain undisturbed. A discussion between the architect and the President on the need for symmetry ended in a fury. Elliot offered to provide a home for the woman for the rest of her life. He argued that his plan covered the entire square, and would be destroyed if built off center. The President was adamant. Fortunately, for aesthetic reasons, the final judgment on this dispute rested with the city commissioners, and they ordered that the building be erected according to the original plans.

This main building was occupied in the Spring of 1840. It didn't seem at the time that any more space would be needed. One classic tale from Patent Office lore tells of an examiner who one day reached for his hat and coat and resigned because everything had already been invented. Although apocryphal, this story's basis in fact was undoubtedly the nearsighted report issued in 1843 by Commissioner Ellsworth. While discussing all the important inventions which had already been made, he stated that "the advancement of the arts, from year to year, taxes our credulity and seems to presage the arrival of that period when human improvement must end." Yet, the

structure soon proved too small for the Commissioner and he complained that the collection of models would force him and his staff into the street. By 1856, the East and West wings were completed with room for exhibiting the models. The excitement generated by the London Crystal Palace Exhibition added to their popularity; it was simply the easiest way to keep up with the latest inventive creation, to see what was new. When the North wing was added, the quadrangle was completed in 1867. The newspapers marked the event with elaborate praise: "the most handsome (building) in the world, so far as architectural proportions are concerned . . . a standing monument to the architectural talent and mechanical ability of the country."

Other changes were also taking place. With the Act of August 29, 1842, "Any person, who, by his own industry, genius, efforts, and expense, has invented any new and original design, may be granted a design patent. George Bruce of New York City received Design Patent Number 1 for printing types. The Act of 1861 extended patents to seventeen years and increased the fee to thirty-five dollars. There was no longer to be any discrimination in fees for foreign applicants. During the Civil War, the decrease in applications warranted the dismissal of many employees. By law, the Office could not operate at a deficit.

The Confederate States of America established their own Patent Commission in the Mechanics Building in Richmond, Virginia, with Rufus B. Rhodes its first and only Commissioner. Two hundred and sixty-six patents were granted despite

Sifting through charred remains of the Patent Office after the fire of September 24, 1877. Fortunately the blaze was confined to two wings containing 160 cases of models, and the destruction was estimated at 76,000 models, a fraction of the collection at the time.

BRINGING MODELS DOWN THE MAIN STAIRWAY

THE FIREMEN AT WORK ON THE ROOF.

GENERAL VIEW OF THE FIRE FROM THE CORNER OF NINTH AND G STREETS.

BURNING OF THE UNITED STATES PATENT OFFICE AT WASHINGTON, D. C., LAST MONDAY.

Rhodes' complaint that "there is not a polytechnic journal for sale at Richmond, and the supply of other books of the kind required by the office is exceedingly limited." Implements of war account for about one-third of the patents.

The end of the War brought a stunning increase in applications, from an average of 6,000 per year to 10,664 in 1865, 15,269 in 1866, and 21,276 in 1867. It was apparent that the system of hiring personnel was inadequate, and Samuel Sparks Fisher, the twelfth Commissioner of Patents, introduced difficult competitive examinations for applicants to his technical staff of examiners. He also required all drawings to conform to a uniform standard, to simplify their reproduction. As insurance against any future disaster, he ordered ten copies of each drawing reproduced by photolithography.

Problems concerning the storage and cataloging of the models continued to increase with their numbers until the confusion was insurmountable. There simply weren't enough clerks to classify, tag, and arrange the models, and the result was a growing clutter filling the display shelves. To remedy this, the Act of July 8, 1870 stipulated that models were no longer required but might be requested by the Commissioner. Unfortunately, many inventors ignored the order, and the collection and confusion continued to grow. Natural causes were, however, once again to cure this ill.

About 11 o'clock in the morning of Sept. 24, 1877, fire again determined the fate of the model collection. A watchman threw a few buckets of water upon discovering the flames, but the drafts in the halls sent the flames through the roof with swift violence, enveloping the neighborhood with smoke. A brisk southern breeze whipped the flames along the roof until the entire West wing was burning.

The women clerks were evacuated, and the men started to empty the offices of all the records. The model room, just beneath the roof was the center of the blaze. The firemen were hampered by the confusion of clerks and citizens breaking cases and running out with models. Postal clerks from across the street also joined in. The streets were crowded with thousands of spectators and materials saved from the burning building.

The Patent Commissioner was out of town, and it was the cool presence and command of former territorial Governor Alexander Shepherd who arrived at the height of confusion that was responsible for saving most of the models and records. He organized the clerks into lines along the staircase leading into the model room, and had them relayed down into the safety of the street, where he placed the police to stand guard.

By two o'clock that afternoon, the fire was under control, and had been confined to the top floor model rooms of the West and North wings. The destruction was estimated at 76,000

SAVING THE RECORDS OF THE LAND OFFICE.   A LITTLE FIRE IN THE LAND COMMISSIONER'S OFFICE

CLERKS PASSING OUT MODELS FROM THE WEST HALL.

PATENT OFFICE PAPERS IN THE ATTIC.

SCENES OF THE FIR

SAVING THE WASHINGTON RELICS.

PATENT OFFICE PAPERS ON THE ROOF.

ASSORTING AND REARRANGING BROKEN MODELS IN THE SOUTH HALL.

SEARCHING FOR MODELS IN THE RUINS OF THE WEST HALL AFTER THE FIRE.

ATTEMPTING TO REMOVE THE OLD FRANKLIN PRESS.

THE UNITED STATES PATENT OFFICE, WASHINGTON, D. C., LAST MONDAY.

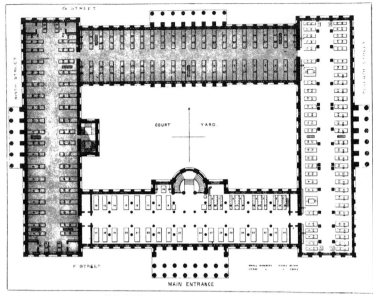

PLAN OF THE MAIN FLOOR OF THE PATENT OFFICE.
[THE SHADED PORTION SHOWS THE EXTENT OF THE FIRE.]

models, mostly of agricultural and mechanical inventions. Congress appropriated $45,000 for their restoration. Amid countless eulogies to the devastated models, the *Scientific American* of Oct. 20, 1877 editorialized that they were a great expense to the inventor, and had become a useless formality. It suggested that the elimination of their requirement would stimulate invention. "There is more sentiment than sense in the oft repeated claim that they constitute a great national museum, wherein the rise and progress of American invention can be studied. All that can be said . . . while some are intrinsically interesting as historical relics, the majority constitute a monument showing only in the aggregate how prolific is the genius of the American inventor."

There is no record of the number of models replaced, but by 1880, the Patent Office was inundated with models. All the storage and exhibit space was taken, and they were haphazardly placed on filing cabinets, desks, book shelves, under chairs, any available space; their influx was so great that the patent law was strengthened to prohibit the sending of any models, except for flying machines, perpetual motion machines, and on specific request.

There was never any attempt to keep any records of the models, but in 1893 Congress allowed the Union Building at 6th and G St. to be rented for their storage.

The models were not without their defenders. Writing of this move, the Patent Office *News* of March 27, 1894, stated: "80,000 of the 154,900 models were removed . . . in order that the space thus vacated might be utilized to meet the urgent demand for additional room to accommodate the working force of the General Land Office and the Patent Office. The

advantage thus gained in room is to a considerable extent offset by the inconvenience to the examiners who have need to inspect these models in their daily work."

Another spokesman for the models was Commissioner Mitchell, in his 1890 report to Congress. "I regard it as nothing less than a public calamity that the Office was several years ago compelled to suspend the reception of models, excepting in special instances, for want of space in which to store and exhibit them . . . I venture to express the hope that the time will come when models will again be required in connection with all applications, and that when that time arrives an effort will also be put forth to obtain specimens of the more important inventions which have been patented during the intervening period.

I recommend Congress to make some provision which will enable the department to return these models to the galleries in this building, designed and constructed for their exhibition."

Congress had been under the mistaken impression that the models were on public display until the Union Building tried to raise the rent in 1907. Congressional investigation discovered there had been no visitors for the year, and took this to indicate a disinterested public. A decision was made to sell the collection after giving the Smithsonian Institution six months to choose those deemed most important.

The resulting selection was debatable then, and is now, in retrospect, deeply regretted by most students of technology. Craddock R. Goins, Jr., Curator of the Division of Military History, feels that they were chosen by someone who only knew or cared about sewing machines. Every curator at the Smithsonian agrees that there was not enough time allowed to properly select such an important collection. Crates were poorly marked for departments, there wasn't enough room to open them all, and, finally, time ran out before a thorough examination was possible. Only 1,061 models were chosen. Three thousand were auctioned off for the sum of $62.18. The rest spent nearly twenty years in odd basements around the Capitol until they were deposited in an abandoned livery stable.

During Calvin Coolidge's economy-minded administration, a Congressional Committee estimated $200,000 had been spent in moving and storage of the collection from 1884 to 1925. The Patent Office had since been transferred to the Department of Commerce, where Herbert Hoover was then Secretary. He urged Congress to appropriate a final $10,000 to dispose of the collection. A three-member board was organized to select models for the Smithsonian and other museums. Inventors and their families were invited to take back their own models.

This time, the Smithsonian acquired about 2500, and other museums and inventors took around 2600. Henry Ford wanted many agricultural and domestic models for his Dearborn museum, and personally supervised the choice of about 25 farm machinery models. These are displayed from time to time at the museum. The original group of men who worked with Thomas Edison were eager to obtain as many of his patent models as possible. Several hundred were bought at a minimal fee, and donated to the Ford Museum, and are housed at the Edison Institute for display and use in research.

A representative assortment was laid out in a Washington warehouse to attract bids, and approximately 50,000 of them brought $1550. The following year the remaining unopened 125,000 crates went to the same buyer for $6,540. There was little competition in the bidding, as the models were in heavy oak packing cases about one cubic yard in size, and presented an enormous shipping and storage problem. The new owner of the collection was Sir Henry Wellcome, a wealthy owner of a pharmaceutical firm who had been knighted by King George V for his services to medicine. He intended to establish a patent museum, a Mecca for all inventors, in Tuckahoe, New York, and had the models shipped to his warehouse there. The stock market crash and the subsequent depression of the 'thirties sounded the death knell to his plans. When he died in 1936 at the age of 82, he was still hopeful; but the crates had never been opened.

The trustees of his estate decided to sell the collection intact, and after two years, found someone to meet their price of $50,000 in Broadway producer, Crosby Gaige. He planned the debut of the collection as carefully as any opening night. Gaige had many of the crates brought to the International Building in Rockefeller Center, where a large crew of workmen pried open the cases and unwrapped the models. On August 8, 1939, he invited several members of the press to observe the operation. An 1860 safe made of crystalized iron appeared, somewhat scarred by jimmy marks and a hole bored through in unsuccessful attempts on its combination. Enter locksmith Charles Courtney, whose nimble fingers twirled the lock for some eight minutes, to tease the crowd and add to the suspense. Suddenly the the tumblers tripped, and the safe doors swung open.

As the crowd pressed closer, Gaige's aides found three obscure patent models. Then, a piece of paper, which in fact was the original application for a patent filed and signed by the most famous patentee of all, Abraham Lincoln. The drawing for Patent #6,469, for Buoying Vessels over Shoals was also included. Gaige's patent models were launched.

Gaige and his partner, entrepreneur Douglas Hertz, kept the press informed of any interesting or amusing models as the unpacking continued. They attracted a lot of publicity, and then, at the height of interest, sold out to a group of businessmen for $75,000. After incorporating as American Patent Models, they sent five hundred objects to be exhibited around the country. Another 24,000 were kept in Rockefeller Center offices, and the rest of the unpacked crates were stored at Neptune Storage Warehouse in New Rochelle, New York.

The new patent model entrepreneurs lacked the imaginative showmanship of Gaige, and with the exception of The Hall of Inventions exhibit at the '39 New York World's Fair, they couldn't excite much interest in their displays. As Neptune Storage filed a lien of $7,954, and Rockefeller Center pressed for its unpaid rent, American Patent Models tried for a quick sale at one dollar each. Many were sold, but in 1942 the group was bankrupt, and abandoned traveling exhibits in Minneapolis, Salt Lake City, and Oakland, California. A court ordered a public auction of the models to pay the storage and warehouse bills.

On May 29, 1942, Bankruptcy Referee John E. Joyce conducted the auction in Foley Square which made O. Rundle Gilbert and his partners the owners of an estimated 200,000 models. After paying $2,100, plus $10,800 to Neptune Storage, and nearly $1,000 to bail out the stranded exhibits, seventy-five trailer truckloads of crates made their way to Gilbert's home in Garrison, New York, where they were stored in several barns in the area.

At the outset, Gilbert, a colorful auctioneer, and his wife had hoped to preserve the collection intact, in search of a benefactor like Wellcome, or an interested museum. Their partners were eager to put them on the block. On April 14, 1943, 2,000 models went on sale at the Architectural League in New York City. The crowd was enormous, but contained only three serious bidders. The result was a disappointing sale of only four hundred models. Gilbert calculated a three thousand dollar loss for the venture.

He and his wife set about the task of unpacking the crates, many of which he felt hadn't been opened since 1908, and had been overlooked by the Smithsonian. By 1945, with the help of a small staff, about 20,000 models were unpacked, identified, classified by category, and made ready for sale. They filled a fourteen-room house on Gilbert's estate, and included several small collections which traced the development of sewing machines, washing machines, and many kinds of hand tools and farm machinery.

In the spring of 1945 as they were preparing announcements of another sale, fire swept through the house, and everything inside was reduced to ashes. The Gilberts were immobilized by the loss, and nothing was done for four more years. In 1949, Gilbert bought a huge barn in Center Sandwich, New Hampshire, and decided to create his own museum for the models. With renewed enthusiasm, crates were opened, models were arranged to show a wide array of inventions: a Gatling gun, a Mergenthaler typesetting machine, countless stoves, boilers, mouse traps. With about 1,000 models on display, the museum was opened, charging admission and attracting an average of seventy-five visitors a day.

But Gilbert's partners weren't content with the prospect of being custodians of the collection, and pressed for more sales. The next attempt was at Gimbels in New York and Philadel-

THE UNITED STATES OF AMERICA

TO ALL TO WHOM THESE PRESENTS SHALL COME:

Whereas, THERE HAS BEEN PRESENTED TO THE

Commissioner of Patents

A PETITION PRAYING FOR THE GRANT OF LETTERS PATENT FOR AN ALLEGED NEW AND USEFUL INVENTION THE TITLE AND DESCRIPTION OF WHICH ARE CONTAINED IN THE SPECIFICATION OF WHICH A COPY IS HEREUNTO ANNEXED AND MADE A PART HEREOF, AND THE VARIOUS REQUIREMENTS OF LAW IN SUCH CASES MADE AND PROVIDED HAVE BEEN COMPLIED WITH, AND THE TITLE THERETO IS, FROM THE RECORDS OF THE PATENT OFFICE IN THE CLAIMANT(S) INDICATED IN THE SAID COPY, AND WHEREAS, UPON DUE EXAMINATION MADE, THE SAID CLAIMANT(S) IS (ARE) ADJUDGED TO BE ENTITLED TO A PATENT UNDER THE LAW.

NOW, THEREFORE, THESE Letters Patent ARE TO GRANT UNTO THE SAID CLAIMANT(S) AND THE SUCCESSORS, HEIRS OR ASSIGNS OF THE SAID CLAIMANT(S) FOR THE TERM OF SEVENTEEN YEARS FROM THE DATE OF THIS GRANT, SUBJECT TO THE PAYMENT OF ISSUE FEES AS PROVIDED BY LAW, THE RIGHT TO EXCLUDE OTHERS FROM MAKING, USING OR SELLING THE SAID INVENTION THROUGHOUT THE UNITED STATES.

In testimony whereof, I have hereunto set my hand and caused the seal of the Patent Office to be affixed at the City of Washington this twenty-ninth day of April, in the year of our Lord one thousand nine hundred and seventy-three, and of the Independence of the United States of America the one hundred and ninety-seventh.

Attest.

Edward *Stotnby Jr.*
Attesting Officer

Robert Rothwell
Commissioner of Patents

phia. Many more crates were opened to provide merchandise for both stores. The newspaper ads assured their readers: GIMBELS IS NUTS OVER PATENT MODELS, YOU'LL BE NUTS OVER THEM TOO! The result was many spectators, and few buyers.

Only about six hundred had been sold since 1942, leaving five thousand odd stranded on the shelves. Gilbert took this opportunity to buy out his partners, and shipped the unsold models to his museum. In 1952, he moved them to an abandoned hospital in Plymouth, New Hampshire for a larger museum. This was in operation until 1970, when Gilbert realized that there was scant hope of a single large museum taking over the entire collection. Various meetings with Smithsonian officials, intent on having them buy back the models, ended with the inconclusive judgment of the curators that since most of the crates were still unopened, they had no way to appraise the collec-

tion. They were all interested to hear of any unexpected treasure which might appear, but unwilling to commit themselves to a blind sale. Gilbert maintained that the prohibitive cost of opening the crates and the subsequent storage and possible restoration of the models were all problems which gave him no choice but to liquidate the collection.

He estimates his own investment since 1942 at one million dollars. There are an undisclosed number of secret barns around Garrison which contain approximately 110,000 models. Gilbert is certain they include many important items which were hastily passed over by the Smithsonian. Now they are being slowly opened to be sold at selected stores, occasional auctions, antique fairs, by mail, and by appointment only at the Patent Model Building in Garrison.

Other collections of models are miniscule in comparison. The Hagley Foundation of Eleutherian Mills in Wilmington, Delaware, has inherited about 700 models from Mr. Tunicliff Fox, who purchased them after the 1939 World's Fair Exhibit. They include models of a more whimsical variety, rather than historical value, such as a sunshade for horses, a combination piano and a bed, and a self-fanning rocking chair. They are regularly assembled for loan exhibits in museums throughout the country.

If the patent models may be called neglected castoff treasures of the Patent Office, the patent application drawings can be considered their abandoned orphans. Required along with the model of the invention, many were primitively rendered in watercolors by the inventor himself. Others were done by professional draughtsmen who sought to place the invention in a living context. The earliest date from 1836 and were executed at the Patent Office's request after the fire, from instructions sent in by the inventors and their families. They were used by the Office in making an official drawing, which was rendered in a uniform manner. Collectively, they comprise a charming social history of the nineteenth century as well as a catalogue of naive art. All the drawings from 1836 to 1871 are in the permanent collection of the National Archives. The later drawings are housed in one of the Patent Office warehouses.

No one can dispute the importance of the models as a record of the inventive genius which Americans have always claimed with pride. Survival in a hostile wilderness and the eventual conquest of the continent depended on an ability to adapt and improve farming equipment and weapons, not to mention necessary advances in transportation, communication, and industry. Unwittingly, however, many of the models are remarkable pieces of American folk art, surpassing the naive intentions of the inventor to reveal a form and spirit worth preserving. The workmanship varies; many of the inventors were carpenters and mechanics, and had their own shops and materials to use for their models. Others less handy, fashioned crudely constructed objects. And yet other budding Edisons and Fords relied on professional patent model makers, who were costly, but assembled a finished model that conceivably could be manufactured.

Some of the models are only a flight of fancy—the wings of a bird man, or a life-preserving coffin. Yet even the absurd evoke dreams and aspirations, sleepless nights, endless tinkering, planning, experimenting, a concentrated effort in search of a better or faster or more efficient manner of doing something. Above all, they testify to a triumph over all the obstacles and ridicule that families and friends seem to reserve for one who is not content with the status quo, but dares to try to improve things, for himself and eventually, for all mankind.

O. Rundle Gilbert, auctioneer and present owner of an estimated 110,000 patent models, in his display building in Garrison, N.Y.

II. The Modelmakers

The patent model was often the homely illustration of an inventor's brainchild, lovingly worked, carefully labeled and sent to the Patent Office for the examiners' verdict regarding originality and prior art. Some were made by the inventors themselves, especially those by such men as Abraham Lincoln, who could not afford the skill of a professional modelmaker. But patent modelmaking was also a serious and a big business which became the almost exclusive domain of artisans able to translate the inventors' ideas and plans into working models. Their advertisements abound in the classified sections of the artisans' and mechanics' journals, the trade papers of the inventor.

To Inventors and Manufacturers

The subscriber would respectfully notify Inventors, that he is prepared to make models of new inventions of any description, in the most perfect manner, and at reasonable rates. Being possessed of a fine stock of tools, especially adapted to the business, and an extensive practical experience in it, he flatters himself that he will be enabled to do full justice to any orders that may be committed to him.

He is also prepared to invent and superintend the construction of machinery adapted to effect particular purposes, and guarantee its successful operation, on terms that may be ascertained by addressing him at his residence, Jersey City, N.J.

For qualifications and abilities he would refer to the editors of *The Inventor.*

John B. Waring

Other modelmakers advertised their specialties: heating, stoves, locomotives, boilers, hot-air furnaces, machinery patents, all done on short notice and on "reasonable" terms.

When William Thornton, Commissioner of Patents, rode on horseback in 1812 to stop the British from burning the patent models, he called on a Mr. Nicholson, his "modelmaker and messenger" to accompany him on his mission. Surely, the modelmaking business was thriving after Congress appropriated funds for the restoration of the models destroyed in the fire of 1836, twenty-four years later.

The making of a model, however, was most often entrusted to a local mechanic. William Gomm was a Rochester machinist who excelled as a modelmaker, and was inventor George Selden's assistant. He helped Selden to conduct his experiments which proved that gasoline was the most effective fuel for the internal combustion engine. In 1876 Selden sent Gomm to the Philadelphia Exhibition to study the engines on view in the German section of Machinery Hall, including several by Brayton, and Otto and Langen. Gomm built the controversial Selden patent model in a few months in 1879, and regretted that the inventor did not feel obliged to order a full scale working model from him.

Washington, D.C., was the natural center for the model industry and it grew tremendously during the mid-nineteenth century. The models themselves confirm the high quality of work executed by these professionals. They were well paid for their craft; many manuals for inventors note that one of the greatest expenses to be expected was the cost of the model. An 1870 manual quotes a rate of 50 cents an hour per man, plus the going market price for material. It also counsels the inventor that a working model of his invention is indispensable to create a favorable impression with a prospective manufacturer, that drawings are of little value to those who can't read them, and that the toylike quality of a model is always fascinating.

When the models were no longer required in 1870, and prohibited except for flying and perpetual motion machines in 1880, the future of the modelmaker was uncertain. But inventors still turned to these craftsmen for tangible evidence of their originality. One Washington, D.C., shop that survived then and still flourishes today is the D. Ballauf Manufacturing Co., founded in 1855.

MANUFACTURE SMALL NOVELTIE NICKEL PLATING DUPLICATES OF PATENT OFFICE MODEL GEAR CUTTING FOR THE TRADE INVENTIONS MADE TO ORDER A MODEL MODEL SHOP RIGHT HANDY W.D.DOREMUS PRACTICAL MECHANICIAN MODEL & LOCK MAKER EXPERT

ROOMS 45 AND 49 DAILY POST BUILDING, WASHINGTON D C

Daniel Ballauf, a hunchback and a bachelor, came to Washington in the early 1800's from what is now East Germany. He bought a row house on 7th Street, N.W., and ran his machine shop in the back. The early records of patent models built by Ballauf and his employees read much like the Patent Office *Gazette* list of new inventions: spyglass, nail machine, crimping machine, clothes wringer, hay fork, gun, bedstead, morticing machine, water wheel, railroad armchair, paper bag machine, churn, locomotive brake, post hole digger, fruit jar, time and speed records, bottle stopper, chain ladder, ice machine, stereoscope, turbine, egg hatcher, turntable, fruit dryer, still, steam plow. Models were made for such inventors as Alexander Graham Bell (experimental work frames for his man-flying kite), Charles Van Depoele (electric motor), Thomas Armat (perforator for motion picture film), Ottmar Mergenthaler (typesetting machine), Emile Berliner (talking machine), and an 1868 McCormick reaper model.

Ballauf was to move his shop to its present location, 619 H Street, N.W., in the rear of another row house. Here he was assisted by a nephew, Adolf Werdemann, and Rudolf

Schneider, another émigré machinist. Schneider eventually became the shop foreman and did most of the work at the firm. In 1894 he married Ballauf's neice, Pauline Heinrich. When the bachelor founder died in 1914, the building and half its stock was left to her; the other half of the tools, machinery, appliances, fixtures and "good will" was entrusted to Werdemann. The Schneider family ran the shop until 1942, and it continued to make patent models on request. It was a lucrative business during these years, with highly skilled worksmanship commanding top prices.

The Ballauf company was both typical and one of the best in Washington. The modelmaking industry seemed to attract skilled German immigrants. Judging from the variety of models produced over the years, they seemed to have been able to execute even the most absurd contraptions. They worked closely with the inventor, often revising as they went along. Inventors crowded the shop when their work was being done, fearing, often with good reason, that someone might steal their novel ideas.

D. BALLAUF,
PRACTICAL MECHANICIAN,
(Established 1855.)

NO. 731 SEVENTH STREET, N.W.,
WASHINGTON, D. C.

Constructor of Light Machinery, Experimental and Model Work.

All orders for Certified Duplicates of Patent Office Models, and Models of any Foreign Patents from Drawings and Specifications, filed in the Library of the Patent Office for law suits in case of infringement; also, Original Models for Inventors, and Models to complete application for Patents, from Drawings and Specifications filed in the Patent Office.

The shop itself was a convivial place. German was the language and beer was furnished by the boss for the customary breaks and with lunch. The traditional beer ration continued until the shop was bought from Rudolf Schneider by Thomas Hayes, one of his employees and now the owner, who felt some of the workers might abuse the available draft, and risk possible injury.

The company outlasted its many competitors because of its commitment to produce unique items. In November, 1885, a special outfit was made for Lieutenant R. E. Peary for the Arctic. They also prepared equipment for Richard Byrd's South Pole expedition. Schneider became a close personal friend of Edison, Bell, Berliner, and worked with C. F. Jenkins, one of the early developers of television. Inventors who could afford to bring their specifications to the Ballauf shop were one giant step ahead of any possible competitor.

An 1894 view of the modelmaking shop of Daniel Ballauf: 1. Oscar Preil, 2. nephew Bill Ballauf, 3. Emil Wagner, 4. nephew Adolf Werdemann, 5. Rudolf Schneider, 6. an unidentified inventor, 7. John Haskins. Werdemann and Schneider ran the business after Daniel Ballauf's death in 1914. The shop is still operated much as it was in the 19th century—except for discontinuation of the beer ration—by Thomas Hayes, a former employee, who bought it from Schneider in 1942. It now specializes in experimental machinery.

1903	Feb. 9-14		
Feb.			
9	Mr. A. G. Bell	6½	} 9
" 6	Tanner combination Lead	2½	
10 ¼	ditto — —	8	} 9
"	Mr. A. G. Bell	1	
11	Tanner Combination Lead	9	
12	ditto — —	6½	
"	Tanner tubes	2½	} 9
13	ditto —	10½	
14	ditto —	5	} 8½
"	Tanner Combination Lead	3½	
	Total	55	
	$ 18.33		

1903	Feb. 16-21		
Feb.			
16	Tanner Tubes	4½	} 12½
"	Tanner Combination Lead	2	
"	Mr. A. G. Bell	6	
17	Max Kuner (Order)	8	} 11
"	Tanner tubes	3	
18	Max Kuner Order Bower	9	
19 New	Thickness gauge	10½	
20	ditto — —	10½	
21	ditto — —	3	} 8½
"	Tanner tubes	5½	
	Total	62	
	$ 20.66		

Time card of a machinist in the Ballauf shop. Alexander Graham Bell is noted as a customer. Bell became a close friend of Rudolf Schneider, and Schneider worked with Bell in making the model for a tetrahedral kite during the inventor's period of aeronautic experimentation. The Tanner sounding tube models were for Captain Z. L. Tanner's invention, a major improvement for navigational soundings.

Modelmaker, Rudolf Schneider, discussing work in 1893 with inventor, Myron Hill, in the Ballauf Manufacturing Co. shop, Washington, D.C. It was the company's policy to demand cash payment in advance from inventors for models of perpetual motion machines.

To the Commissioner of Patents.

The Petition of *Abraham Lincoln, of Springfield in the county of Sangamon & State of Illinois* Respectfully represents.

That your petitioner *has* invented, *a new and improved manner of combining adjustable buoyant chambers with steam boats or other vessels* which ha s not, as *he* verily believes been heretofore used or known, and that he *is* desirous that Letters Patent of the United States may be granted to *him* therefor, securing to *him* and to *his* legal representatives, the exclusive right of making and using, and of vending to others the privilege to make or use, the same, agreeably to the provisions of the Acts of Congress in that case made and provided, *he* having paid *thirty* dollars into the Treasury of the United States, and complied with other provisions of the said Acts.

And *he* hereby authorises and empowers *his* Agent and Attorney, Z. C. ROBBINS, to alter or modify the within specification and claim as he may deem expedient, and to receive *his* patent; and also to receive back any moneys which *he* may be entitled to withdraw, and to receipt for the same.

A. Lincoln.

County of Washington
District of Columbia } ss.

On this *10th* day of *March 1849* before the subscriber, a *Jus Peace* in and for the said *county* personally appeared the within named *Abraham Lincoln* and made solemn *oath* according to law, that *he believes himself* to be the original and first inventor of the within described *improved manner of combining buoyant chambers with steam boats or other vessels and* that *he does* not know or believe that the same has been before used or known; and that *he is a* citizen of the United States.

6469-2

Left, The application submitted to the Patent Office by Abraham Lincoln for the device he believed would revolutionize shipping on the nation's inland waterways. Unfortunately, like most of the models submitted during this time, its ultimate use was as a display item—the only patent model executed by a President of the United States.

Right, Horse Sewing Machine, James Perry, New York, N.Y., Nov. 23, 1858, Patent No. 22,148. The inventor submitted an application for patenting mechanical improvements in the looper, feeder, and tension; the brass horse was not mentioned. Perhaps the movement of the treadle suggested the steady, dependable rhythm of hoofbeats. A remarkable piece of American folk art, this model was never duplicated in production. It is one of the many examples of the inventor's art in which originality of design has transcended in importance any claim of technological improvement.

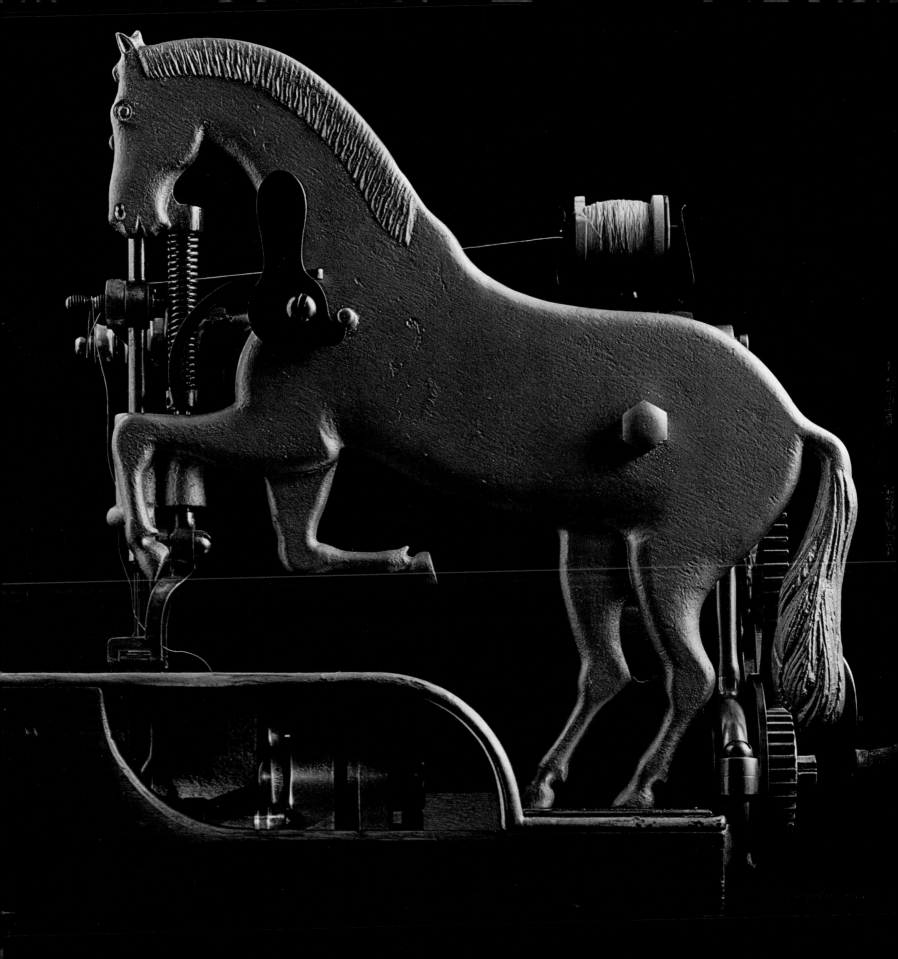

Smoke Conveyor, John S. Thomas, St. Louis, Mo., Sept. 14, 1874, Patent No. 156,187. Belching smoke and sparks were among the hazards endured by train passengers of the 1870's. The solution offered in this invention is a filtered exhaust pipe extending the length of the train. The front end of the pipe has a jointed cap which fits over the top of the chimney, and the discharge of pollution is accelerated by the partial vacuum caused by the forward motion of the train.

From top left, clockwise, **Burial Urn,** "The Home of a Deceased Friend," inventor, date, and patent number unknown. **Lifeboat Improvement,** George Tremberger and Michael Stein, New York, N.Y., June 14, 1878, Patent No. 211,807. A vessel with a cylindrical, revolving passenger cabin which would remain stable regardless of turbulence. It was also equipped with a telescopic mast, hand pumps, fog horn, propeller, rudder, steering wheel. **Metal Boat,** Joseph Francis, New York, N.Y., Mar. 23, 1858, Patent No. 19,693. A peculiar form of corrugated metal useful in making boats of many dimensions from the same dies. **Improved Combined Pistol-Sword,** August Rauh, Westphalia, Prussia, Feb. 16, 1866, Patent No. 52,504. A 36" cavalry saber in an iron scabbard with a six-chambered, .40 caliber revolver. **Steamboat Steering Gear,** Frederick E. Sickles, New York, N.Y., May 10, 1853, Patent No. 9713. The earliest steam steering gear, exhibited at the Crystal Palace, London, 1851.

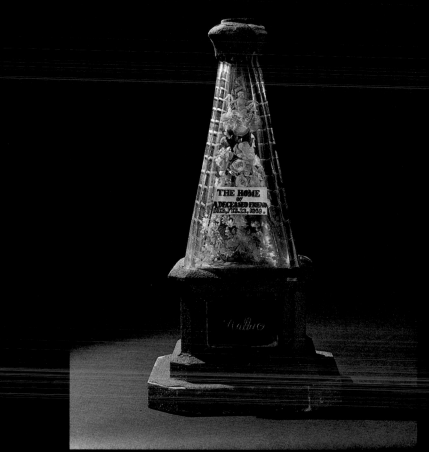

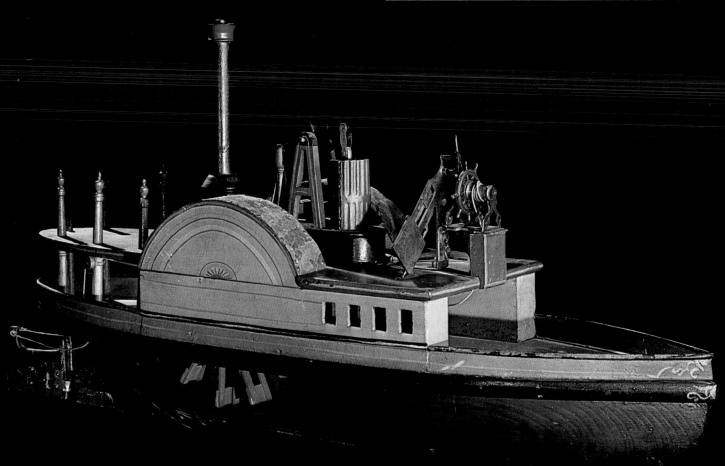

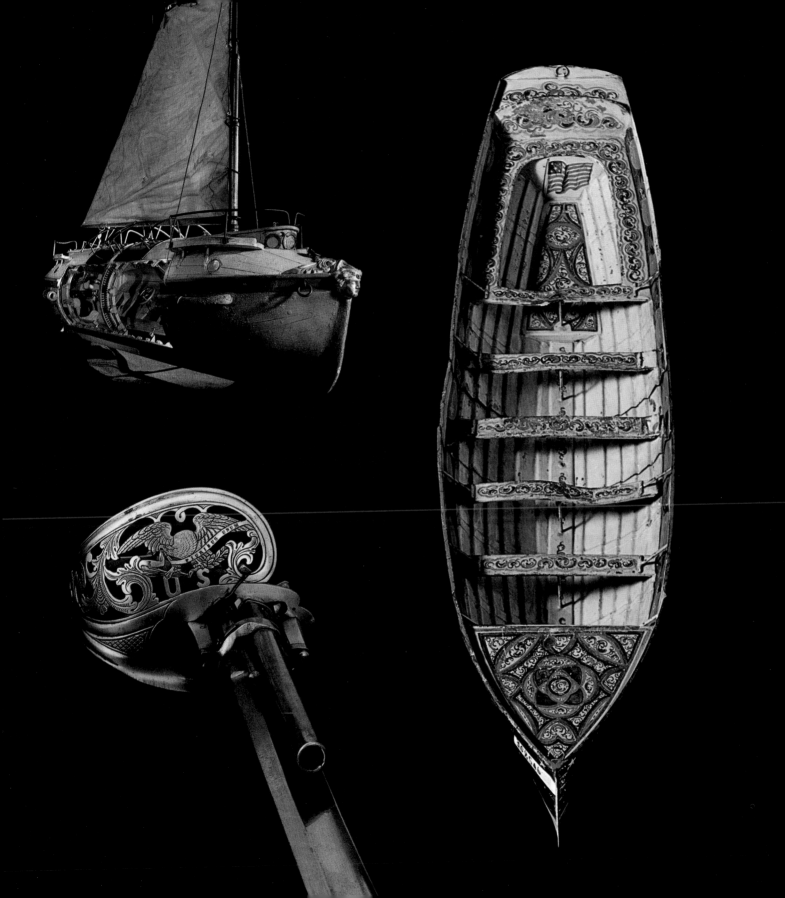

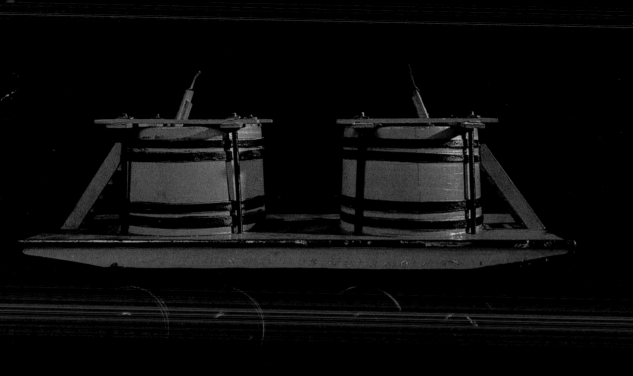

for Locomotives, Milton V. Nobles, Elmira, N.Y., Jan. 11, 1873, Patent No. 137,472. The mechanism is used to sand the drive wheels of locomotives attempting steep grades, braking, or whenever additional friction was needed. Steam from the boiler moistens the sand for better adherence to the wheels. **Grade-Climbing Locomotive,** G. E. Sellers, Cincinnati, Ohio, July 9, 1850, Patent No. 7,498. A solid walnut model demonstrating an improvement in boiler and gearing of locomotives working heavy grades, which insures the alternate action of the two engines on the auxiliary drivers. **Combined Starting and Blow-Off Valve,** Samuel Vauclain, Philadelphia, Penn., Dec. 7, 1891, Patent No. 414,836. By combining cylinder cocks with the starting valves of a compound engine, Vauclain dispensed with one set of levers and connections and simplified the driving mechanism.

The average American inventor was probably more like Abraham Lincoln; he could not afford the assistance of a professional modelmaker. In September, 1848, after finishing his first session in Congress, Lincoln decided to return home by way of Niagara Falls and the Great Lakes. As Lincoln later described his trip to William Herndon, somewhere on Lake Erie the steamer became grounded on a sand bar. As he watched by the rail, the captain ordered all hands to gather empty barrels and boxes and force them under the sides of the ship below the water line. Slowly the vessel started to rise off the sand bar, and Lincoln took out a piece of paper and began to make sketches of what he had just seen. When he reached Springfield he set out at once to build a model and to refine the idea. Observers at the time have recalled seeing Lincoln whittle out an 18″ model from red cedar, using tools from the shop of Walter Davis.

If effective, Lincoln's novel invention could be put to immediate use either on the Sangamon River, then a barely navigable stream, or along the hundreds of other waterways which provided such an important link in early transportation. A public demonstration of the idea was announced in John Williams' general store, and before a curious crowd Lincoln placed his model boat in a watering trough in the public square. Putting bricks on it until water reached the gunwalls, he proceeded to fill the two side compartments with air by means of a bellows. The boat laden with bricks rose in the water, and Lincoln explained that if the air compartments were filled, any boat could be lifted off a sand bar.

Left, Selden Car, George Selden, Rochester, N.Y., Nov. 5, 1895, Patent No. 549,160. Selden, a patent attorney, kept his application alive for 16 years, during which time the automobile developed into a practical reality. He made subtle additions in his claims to include all the developments in the industry up to 1895. His opponent was Henry Ford, at the time a relative David engaged in battle with the Goliath Selden monopoly. The patent model itself, as noted in Chapter 3, was important evidence in the court battles between the two which ended in Ford's favor in 1911. At that time, it was determined that Selden was describing a Brayton-type mechanism for his internal combustion engine. Ford had, however, favored the Otto-type engine which Selden, in a diary, had dismissed as "another of those damned Dutch engines."

Shortly after returning to Washington in 1849 he met Zenas C. Robbins, a patent lawyer from St. Louis who was very familiar with the construction and equipment of riverboats. Robbins was convinced that Lincoln's idea was a sound and patentable one. Lincoln proceeded with the necessary application and drawings, submitted the homely, varnished model, and was granted patent Number 6469 on May 22, 1849. It was first displayed at the Patent Office, and now occupies a place of honor in the National Museum of History and Technology of the Smithsonian Institution. The invention itself was never manufactured.

Although Lincoln shared the fate of so many inventor/tinkerers, he did not lose his enthusiasm for an imaginative and novel new object. This interest was to increase during the Civil War years when improvements in weapons were so important. He had become a good friend of scientist and Smithsonian head, Joseph Henry, and the Swedish inventor, John Ericsson. It was with Lincoln's encouragement and permission that the ironclad "Monitor" was built, and only at his insistence was the Spencer repeating rifle adopted by the Army. When Christopher Spencer brought his latest rifle to Lincoln, they tried it out on practice targets at the Washington Monument; Lincoln hit a bull's-eye.

His kind reception of inventors brought in a fair share of impractical brainchildren through the White House doors. One proposed a pair of water tight "canoes" for soldiers' feet which would eliminate a need for bridges. Another suggested ironclad balloons for moving artillery. An alleged bullet proof steel vest evoked the suggestion from Lincoln that the inventor wear it while sharpshooters tested its strength. After one inventor demonstrated a material which would "burn the rebels" by setting fire to some wooden barrels, Lincoln watched the smouldering pieces of wood and said, "Can't you invent something to burn bricks, mortar, earth works or even green grass. Up to this date, our armies find no difficulty in burning wood."

When Lincoln delivered a speech entitled "Discoveries and Inventions" in 1860, he referred to the Bible for inspiration. The first discovery made by man, he declared, was that he was naked, and the first invention, the fig leaf. However absurd the situation—and laughter was a most important discovery, too—the inventor, the innovator must be encouraged. He believed that the "Patent system added the fuel of interest to the fire of genius." And for Americans, the only tolerable old things not needing improvement were whiskey and tobacco.

THE MODEL-MAKER.—Drawn by A. R. Waud.—[See Page 210.]

III. Selden vs. Ford

"Selden can take his patent and go to hell with it!"

Although this challenge has often been attributed to Henry Ford, it was James Couzens, his outspoken secretary-treasurer, who threw down the gauntlet. Couzens roared out his reply after Ford and his men heard out the demands of the Selden monopoly in 1903. Everyone in the room turned toward Henry Ford, who was then dangling in a chair tilted against the wall. He confirmed his assent with, "Couzens has answered you."

Thus began one of the most complex and drawn-out patent battles in American history. The litigation involved the use of models, in particular, and the testimony of hundreds of individuals. Above all, it confirmed the great importance of an inventor's documenting his claim to patent protection with every possible device. The original patent commissioners had not been wrong when they stipulated that a working model was essential for evaluation *and* protection.

George Selden, a Rochester, New York, patent attorney, began studying the self-propelled vehicle in the early 1870's. In 1879, with the help of a modelmaker and mechanic, William Gomm, he built a three-cylinder motor, an improvement on the "two-stroke-cycle" engine introduced by George Brayton of Boston in 1873. Against Gomm's advice, a working model was not made but only one designed to give the general concept of a gasoline-driven automobile. Perhaps Selden thought that, as a specialist in patent litigation, he could surely protect himself from any possible trouble. His most famous legal client was his friend, George Eastman, and Selden saw that Eastman's application for an improved process for coating gelatine dry plates was properly handled.

Eastman was a witness to Selden's 1879 application to cover the new motor. Selden knew that he could amend his application as many times as he wanted to during a seventeen-year period, and this he did at least 100 times between 1879 and 1895. As he changed and amended his application, he enlarged his claims to cover all types of compression gas engines. By 1895 the Selden vehicle was obsolete, but a perfect legal invention by a shrewd patent lawyer. And by this time, other engines—by Gottlieb Daimler and Karl Benz—were in use. Selden thought they were all indebted to him, and intended to prove it.

NOTICE

To Dealers, Importers, Agents and Users of

GASOLINE AUTOMOBILES

We will protect you against any prosecution for alleged infringements of patents. Regarding alleged infringement of the Selden patent we beg to quote the well-known Patent Attorneys, Messrs. Parker & Burton. "The Selden patent is not a broad one, and if it was it is anticipated. It does not cover a practicable machine, no practicable machine can be made from it and never was so far as we can ascertain. It relates to that form of carriage called a FORE CARRIAGE. None of that type have ever been in use, all have been failures." "No court in the United States has ever decided in favor of the patent on the merits of the case, all it has ever done was to record a prior agreement between the parties."

We are the pioneers of the GASOLINE AUTOMOBILE. Our Mr. Ford made the first Gasoline Automobile in Detroit and the third in the United States. His machine made in 1893 is still in use. Our Mr. Ford also built the famous "999" Gasoline Automobile, which was driven by Barney Oldfield in New York on Saturday a mile in 55 4-5 seconds on a circular track, which is the world's record.

Mr. Ford, driving his own machine, beat Mr. Winton at Grosse Pointe track in 1901. We have always been winners.

FORD MOTOR COMPANY,

688-692 Mack Ave., Detroit, Mich.

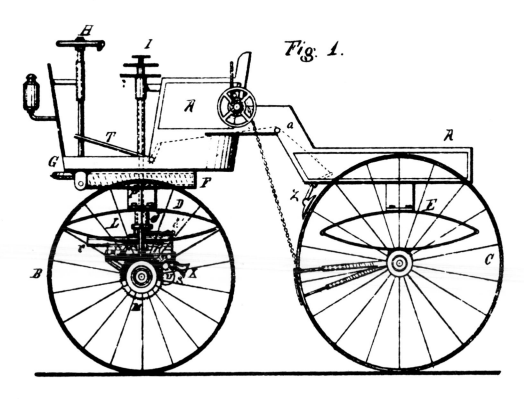

G. B. SELDEN.
ROAD ENGINE.

No. 549,160.

Patented Nov. 5, 1895.

Fig. 1.

In 1899 the Columbia and Electric Vehicle Company, which was ready to manufacture electric taxi cabs for many cities, bought control of the Selden patent for $10,000, and a royalty percentage of sales and licenses. Other companies were informed by Columbia that they were infringing *the* patent. In 1900 Columbia sued the leading manufacturer of the day, the Winton Motor Carriage Co. Winton reacted by organizing nineteen other manufacturers in opposition, and incorporating them as the Hydrocarbon Motor Vehicle Manufacturers Association. This suit was finally resolved in March, 1903, when Winton decided, with five other manufacturers, to buy out the Selden/Columbia patent. The six, known as the Association of Licensed Automobile Manufacturers, then turned to a new prey—Henry Ford's young company.

Ford's attorney, the colorful Razelmond A. Parker of Detroit, was sure that the Selden claim was worthless. He felt that the "invention" had been anticipated in other forms, and that since the courts had never really decided the case, the Selden claim was virtually untried. Ford was quoted as saying that he would gladly give the Association $1000 to

start the suit, and that he would find the resultant publicity most valuable. Finally, five suits were initiated and combined for purposes of a decision.

The trial, presided over by Judge Charles Merrill Hough, in New York's Court of Appeals, began in 1909 after five years had been spent documenting both sides of the case. The trial took two months, and resulted, to everyone's surprise, in a decision for Selden. Ford's main argument was that his car was based on a totally different engine than that of Selden, one predating by many years any possible Selden contribution. The Selden brief was simplistic and ignored any evidence of prior art, and denied that the patent had been altered to include technical changes between 1879 and 1895. This appeal seemed to suit Judge Hough. He accepted the idea that all internal combustion engines were the same and were included in the Selden patent, and the wily patent lawyer/inventor was vindicated.

During this time the Association of Licensed Automobile Manufacturers initiated over 70 suits for infringement, and made numerous threats to collect back royalties. Every suit

George Selden with his Selden Buggy. Only two were built according to the specifications of his patent for demonstrations during the litigation. The "77" painted on the side particularly annoyed Henry Ford's lawyer, Razelmond Parker, because he felt it gave the impression that it was built in 1877. In truth, most of the engine parts were made after 1904. As Exhibit 89 and Exhibit 157, the two prototypes demonstrated on a race track near Guttenberg, N. J., beginning June 14, 1907, that with a team of engineers and a starting shed on a raised platform, the maximum distance traveled by either model, with two stops en route, was 3,450 feet.

awaited Judge Hough's decision. When it came, the ALAM moved quickly to collect the fruits of victory. But Hough's decision was not to be sustained. It was appealed by Ford, and on January 9, 1911, the presiding judge of the New York Court of Appeals, Walter Chadwick Noyes, read a decision in favor of Ford. He noted that there was no invention involved in the use of a gas engine or liquid hydrocarbon gas engine in a motor vehicle; both the Otto and Brayton gas-driven engines existed in 1879. He conceded that Selden had made several inprovements and had advanced many ideas for the automobile, but, that judging from a vehicle constructed from the patent specifications Selden couldn't be given credit for any major breakthrough. *If*, the Judge declared, Selden had "appreciated the superiority of the Otto engine and adopted that type for his combination, his patent would cover the modern automobile. He did not do so . . . and we cannot, by placing any forced construction upon the patent, make another choice for him at the expense of these defendants, who neither legally nor morally owe him anything."

The court fees for the losers were conservatively estimated at $500,000, and these were paid by the ALAM. George Selden had started to manufacture his own vehicle in 1906,

and his company soon collapsed. With it he lost most of the $600,000 he had collected in Columbia, then Winton, and, finally, ALAM royalties. Ford emerged the winner in every respect. He was seen by the public as a giant killer, a David willing to wager his slim resources on a battle against monopoly, and economic repression. It was the best publicity Ford ever was to receive.

The industry was then ready to develop along less litigious lines. By 1913 more than 485,000 motor cars were being produced. With so many competing inventors and engineers, and with the Selden case so freshly in mind, the Automobile Manufacturers Association was established in 1915, and with it a free patent pool to be shared by all. The pool was in effect until after World War II, when it was felt unnecessary to continue it. While it saved the manufacturers any possible legal costs, it left the individual inventor without any hope of profiting from a single invention for the industry. He had become a member of a salaried research team.

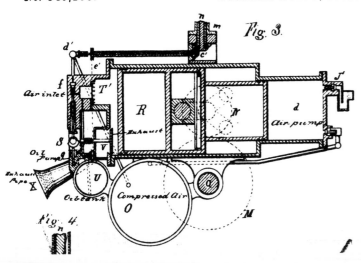

G. B. SELDEN.
ROAD ENGINE.

No. 549,160.   Patented Nov. 5, 1895.

Otto Engine, Nicolaus August Otto, Deutz, Germany, Aug. 14, 1877, The "silent Otto," here represented by a patent model, anticipated the standard internal combustion engine. The model includes a fly wheel to regulate its four-stroke operation in a single cylinder with a slide-valve flame ignition. After being exhibited at the Paris Exposition of 1878, it was recognized as being a truly superior engine. Its manufacture in the United States began in 1882 and nearly every automobile manufacturer in Europe and America, with the exception of Selden, adopted it. Patent No. 194,047.

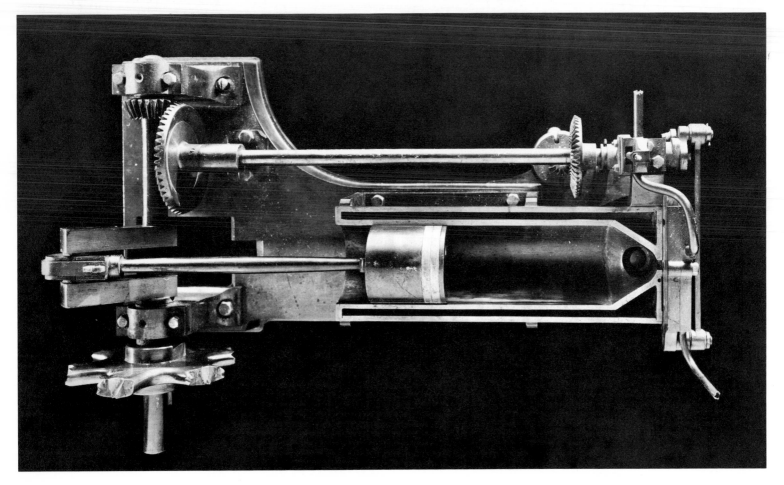

Brayton Engine, George B. Brayton, Boston Mass., June 2, 1874. Until "silent Otto" emerged, this was the favorite, the most promising of internal combustion engines. It was exhibited at the Philadelphia Exhibition in 1876. Patent No. 151,-468.

IV. Establishing Momentum

The American clock industry emerged in the early 1800's from the workshops of New England mechanics who combined the skills of a blacksmith, engraver, cabinetmaker, foundryman, mechanic and, occasionally, an artist. He was also a watch repairman who made weathervanes, tools, toys, scales, printing presses, bells, buttons, surveyor's instruments and wooden nutmegs. The first Yankee clockmakers were also the first Yankee peddlers, often accepting payment in clothing, lumber, or any other available commodity. They are among the first important group of American inventors. In both technological and economic terms, they provided the momentum necessary to launch the industrial revolution in America.

Gideon Roberts (1749-1813) of Fall Mountain, Conn., was typical of the first generation. He made columns and pinions on a foot lathe, cut out the wheels with a jackknife and handsaw, then pasted on a dial and hand face which he had drawn on paper. After finishing a few of these clocks, he set out on his horse to peddle them in the neighboring counties. His sons apprenticed with him and eventually took over the business.

Eli Terry of Plymouth, Conn., was more enterprising, and is sometimes called the father of the clock industry. He originally sold his clocks on horseback, like Roberts, but as his business grew, Terry moved production to a power mill and set up rigging machinery which enabled him to produce clocks at a lower cost. In 1806 he filled the first order for a mass-produced peacetime item; four thousand clocks were assembled. In 1814 Terry invented the pillar scroll top shelf clock, an item which replaced the hanging wooden clock in many homes and offices. He sold the patent rights to Seth Thomas, a young West Haven, Connecticut, mechanic and a partner, for $1,000. By 1825 both were making and selling approximately 10,000 to 12,000 clocks a year, each selling for $15.

Joseph Ives of Bristol, Connecticut, advanced the development of early American clock manufacturing yet further. Better known in Bristol as "Uncle Joe," Ives started making wooden movements in partnership with his five brothers, Ira, Chauncey, Shaylor, Philo and Amasa, in a workshop on Federal Street. In 1815 they set up a manufacturing plant in North Village, on Mine Brook. Three years later Joseph invented and manufactured a metal clock, with iron plates and brass wheels. Unfortunately, it was too large (it needed a five-foot case) and cumbersome to be commercially successful. In 1822 Ives made a brass shelf clock, with a mirror, which was known as the "bronze looking glass clock," and this was a more feasible model.

Ives was the first to use rolled sheet brass, a substance which had many advantages over wood. It took a full year to season wood for wheels and plates. A factory could produce only about 10,000 wooden parts per year, even with the use of a circular saw. Wood was also impractical for exportation as the parts and cases swelled and warped en route. With sheet brass, wheels and parts could be stamped out with dies.

Joseph Ives' invention of the eight-day brass clock, manufactured by his brothers in 1832, was responsible for the great expansion of the industry. The clock work was submitted to the Patent Office to illustrate an improvement for pinion rolling and a pinion wheel, and was patented on April 12, 1833. Ives also invented the movement for a thirty-day brass clock and, according to his contemporary Chauncey Jerome, "spent most of his time for the next twenty-five years in improving on springs and escapements for clocks, and has done a great deal for the advancement of this business."

The eight-day clock sold for about $20, and netted nearly $100,000 for the Ives brothers—until the Panic of 1837. At that time they, along with many other manufacturers, lost their assembly plants. But it was only a temporary loss.

Chauncey Jerome, a supreme egomaniac and author of *History of the American Clock Business for the Past 60 Years and Life of Chauncey Jerome,* set the new course for the business. Up to this time there had been a fixed idea that wooden clocks should be one-day, and brass, eight-day. In 1838 Jerome conceived the idea for a cheap, one-day brass clock which his brother, Noble, developed and patented. Jerome, who had lost one fortune in the Panic, made himself another and, according to his own record, "put more than a million of dollars into the pockets of the brass makers. . . ." He also developed a booming export business, with China as one of the major markets.

Improvement in Striking Mechanism of Clock, Joseph Ives, Bristol, Conn., April 12, 1833. Although the written specification sheet is lost, the patent was reviewed in the October, 1833, issue of the *Journal of the Franklin Institute.* As described there, the clock featured a count wheel which would revolve once instead of twice in twenty-four hours. This was achieved by doubling the number of notches in the circumference of the wheel. Unimpressed by Ives' claims, *The Journal* went on to observe that the same improvement was currently available in Italy.

The family register of Amasa Ives and Huldah Shaylor, whose six sons were important to the clock-making industry of America. Ira, Joseph and Chauncey were the inventors. The other three brothers, Shaylor, Philo and Amasa, were less mechanical, but in partnership with the others established a thriving manufactory in Bristol, Conn., which produced buttons and clocks.

In the meantime Joseph Ives and his son, Porteous, bought a new mill site at Plainville, on the Pequatuck River, the nearest point to Bristol on the Farmington Canal. Several businessmen from the "Bristol Basin" advanced money in hopes of reestablishing the clock industry. It was here that Ives manufactured the "hour glass clock." Its wholesale cost was $12, considered an extravagance, and relatively few were made. Again, in 1842, Ives had to face bankruptcy proceedings, but he never ceased making improvements. In 1845 he patented an "elliptical spring" known as the "wagon spring" powered movement. It was bought by one of the two firms in Bristol which were producing clocks for foreign and/or national markets, Birge & Fuller. Ives' seventh and last patent, Number 25,934, was granted when he was 77-years-old for a "Watch." In the specifications he explained that he "was aware that a feeling of absurdity will at first strike the mind of the observer, but a moment's careful reflection will show . . . that the inventive mind has been called into careful exercise . . . . " Ives died in his 80th year, in 1862, having witnessed the development of an industry from the assembling of a clock by a single skilled artisan to those mass-produced by relatively unskilled workmen.

It is possible to present a convincing thesis that the clock, and not the steam engine, is the key to the modern industrial age. Although man measured time with water and sand, by the sun and stars, it was only after the development of the wheel, weight, gears and escapement that an accurate mechanical clock was feasible. The water clock, or clepsydra, was the first standard measurement which combined

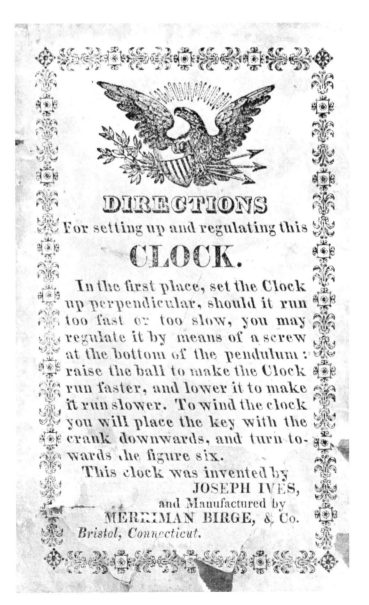

several gear combinations with good results. It was commonly used from early Roman times through the thirteenth century. Subsequent developments permitted inventors to think in terms of transmitting and regulating motion, of controlling speed through gears, translating rotary movement to reciprocal movement, and the dividing of equal units of time and space.

Also, the "modern" clock necessitated precision of parts heretofore unrequired. Handmade tools were not sufficiently well-executed for the construction of a smooth working timepiece. Machines to make exact parts were created, rendering the "interchangeable parts" theory a possibility.

By 1800 the elegant drawing rooms of America's growing cities were furnished with fine examples of the European clockmaker's art. Individual makers in such cities as Boston and Philadelphia, followed the Old World methods with considerable skill. But it took the practical and mechanical genius of Chauncey Jerome and Joseph Ives to supply the American farmer with accurate and inexpensive clocks, transforming these items from the category of luxury to necessity. Jerome's success in mass production created one of America's first manufacturing export businesses. The declared value of his first shipment to England was considered so preposterously low that it was confiscated by British customs who suspected a ruse to avoid paying duty. When they received a second shipment in record time with the same low declared value, they were forced to acknowledge the possibility of such a feat of production.

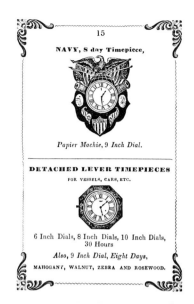

INTRODUCTION.

Within the last few years, the manufacture of Clocks has become an important branch of American Industry.

Clocks are not, as many persons appear to imagine, "ground out" in a Mill; neither are they wholly manufactured by Machinery, but each one passes through two hundred processes in the hands of workmen before it is completed.

That most expensive and perfect Machinery is required is very true, and it is also true that with all proper requisites, and a full knowledge of the business, in all its details, great attention and care is necessary to make good Clocks. That most of those now made are good and reliable "Time-keepers" is a fact generally known. There are some inferior establishments, which are not only deficient in proper machinery, but in all the essential facilities for manufacturing, and it is not strange that some worthless Clocks find their way to market. Certain unscrupulous dealers, unable to push their wares into market in an honest way, have been so base as to counterfeit the labels of respectable manufacturers, and not long since a party of these worthies had a verdict of twenty-seven hundred dollars rendered against them, for perpetrating this fraud. As other suits are now pending, it is to

be hoped that this system of piracy will soon be stopped

Those purchasers who desire not to be imposed upon will see the importance of buying those which bear the name of some well-known manufacturer, and at a regular establishment.

Improvement in manufacturing is still the order of the day. Many new and beautiful patterns have recently been brought into market, and, as it is impossible to convey an idea of the same to our distant friends, by any written description, we have found it necessary to prepare a set of engravings, as the best plan of showing the various patterns.

The attention of the Trade is particularly invited to the styles herein represented, which embrace all the leading patterns of the day; among them will be found those suitable for Public Buildings, Churches, Banks, Stores, Ships, Steamboats, Rail Road Cars, Parlors, Halls and Kitchens. Purchasers for foreign markets will be furnished with any styles that may be desired. In addition to those herein represented we have many other styles of Clocks. We shall at all times be prepared to fill orders for any new patterns that may be introduced, all of which will be sold at the very lowest market rates for Cash.—Respectfully,

JEROME & CO.

8
HEIGHT, 25 INCHES.

EXTRA COLUMN also Alarms.

OCTAGON, EIGHT DAY.

12 Inch Dial, Striking, and 10 Inch Time Piece,
MAHOGANY AND ROSEWOOD.

15

NAVY, 8 day Timepiece,

Papier Machie, 9 Inch Dial.

DETACHED LEVER TIMEPIECES
FOR VESSELS, CARS, ETC.

6 Inch Dials, 8 Inch Dials, 10 Inch Dials,
30 Hours

Also, 9 Inch Dial, Eight Days,
MAHOGANY, WALNUT, ZEBRA AND ROSEWOOD.

Pages from trade catalog issued by Chauncey Jerome which advertises clocks "suitable for Public Buildings, Churches, Banks, Stores, Ships, Steamboats, Railroad Cars, Parlors, Halls, and Kitchens."

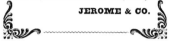

Hour Glass Clock, Joseph Ives, Bristol, Conn., c. 1839-1842. An extremely rare item then, and more so today; few of the clocks were produced. Because of its unusual design, the size of the movement was restricted to a thirty-hour spring, rather than a weight-operated movement. This made the clock portable, but it did not offset the added manufacturing costs.

The Art of Invention

From Sad Irons to Reversible Barber Chairs

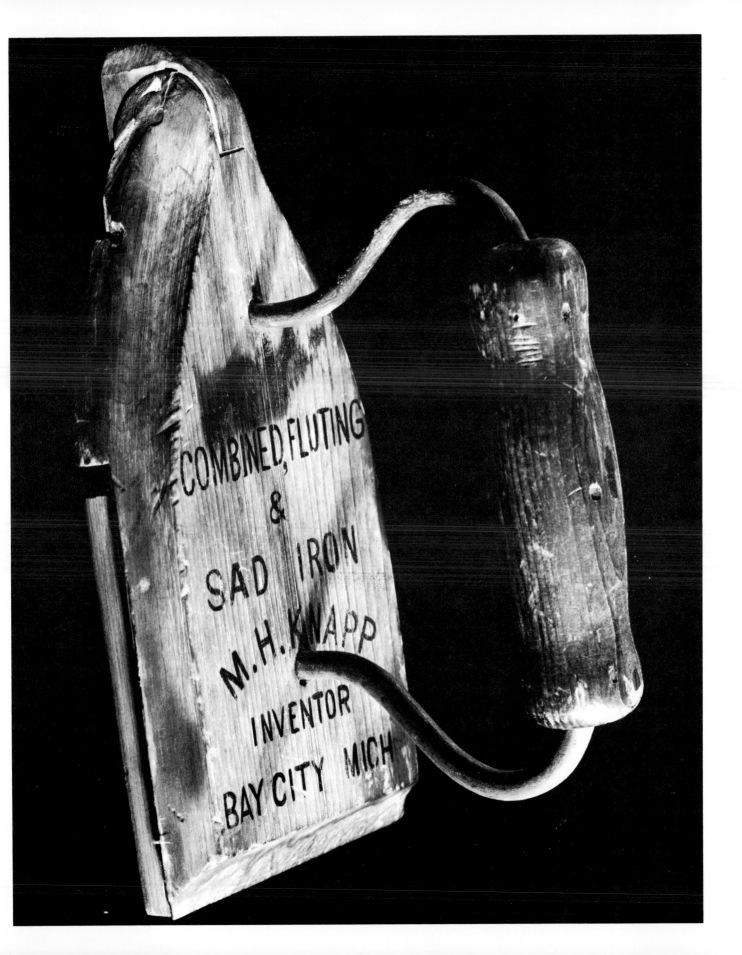

V. All Around the House

In the beginning of *A Connecticut Yankee in King Arthur's Court,* sometime inventor Mark Twain describes the pride and spirit that prevailed in the nineteenth century among lone mechanics and tinkerers:

Why, I could make anything a body wanted—anything in the world, it didn't make any difference what; and if there wasn't any quick new-fangled way to make a thing, I could invent one—and do it as easy as rolling off a log.

And so it was. The New England inventor, in particular, produced item after item for the home, simple comforts for the individual, his home, and labor and time-saving devices for the housewife.

For obvious reasons, servants were never easy to find in America. For the first time the "lady" of the house, however educated and genteel, might be solely responsible for her own housework. Americans referred to their paid labor as "help" in the cities, and "hired hands" on the farm. There were no "servants," except in the South and some large cities. The average New Englander, with no "help" to be hired, developed a reputation for finding the shortest, most expedient method of performing chores, allowing time for reading, sewing, needlework and drawing. Every bride brought to her new abode sheets, table cloths of her own weaving, embroidery, patchwork quilts, curtains, and, of course, clothing of her own making. The New England housewife, and all those like her across the country, firmly believed that "ORDER is Heaven's First Law."

Farsighted Jefferson hoped for relief for the homemaker, and proposed in 1815 the use of small portable steam engines which could "wash the linen, knead the bread, beat the hominy, churn the butter, turn the spit, and do all other household offices which require only a regular mechanical motion." His demand was met all through the nineteenth century by inventors with patents for washing machines, egg beaters, apple corers, clothes pins, dishwashers, carpet sweepers, iron stoves. By 1873 the Patent Office had granted more than 2,000 patents for an "improved clothes washer." Many of these designs were surprisingly modern, although all lacked the electric motor.

The first modern carpet fan sweeper was invented in 1859, and the first successful model was patented by Melville Bissell in 1876. The modern-design washing machine was invented in 1869, the dishwasher in 1865, and the vacuum cleaner in 1859. There were hundreds of designs for paring, coring and slicing apples—that all-American fruit—and hardware manufacturers and dealers pushed them with great success.

Hundreds of ideas were proposed for a sewing machine in the first half of the nineteenth century. The earliest were patented by John J. Greenough in 1842 (never produced) and an unsuccessful model patented by George H. Corliss in 1843. Elias Howe, Jr., achieved success in 1846. He did not claim to have invented the eye-pointed needle, but rather combined a curved eye-pointed needle with a shuttle to form a lockstitch with an intermittent feed.

Howe had as much trouble in securing orders for his new machine as did Otis with the elevator. He demonstrated it in public halls and clothing factories in the Boston area in the late 1840's—without much success. Howe then moved on to England and after considerable difficulty, sold his British patent rights to an umbrella manufacturer, William Thomas, for a mere 250 pounds. Howe, in effect, pawned his patent for return passage to America. Upon returning in 1849 he discovered that many sewing machines, more or less based on his design, were being sold with great financial success. Isaac Singer was among those who allegedly had "borrowed" from Howe, and after a drawn-out court battle, the Singer Sewing Machine Company was ordered by the court to pay Howe $15,000, plus a royalty on each machine sold. Eventually, all the sewing machine companies reached an agreement to pool their patents. As in the automobile business later, it became a necessity.

Opposite page, Combined Sad and Fluting Iron, M. H. Knapp, Bay City, Mich., Aug. 2, 1870. The iron is constructed in two sections, on two levels, which could be used either for fluting or as a regular iron. Patent No. 105,953.

The inventor of home improvements had a particular love for combining several different functions within a single or easily changed mechanism. With the flick of the wrist the sad iron becomes a fluting iron, the step ladder an ironing board. Judging from the patent drawings, a bed could be stored and ready for use nearly anywhere inside an upright piano, in a wardrobe, the sofa, or even in the fireplace. But most of all, the inventor sought ways to save time, labor and space, and to make himself and his fellow men more comfortable. The cold of winter could be thrown off with the use of a portable radiator, decorated to fit the decor. The heat of summer was cooled with a mechanical fan. Tending the fire was made easier with a tiny door in the screen. The possibilities were endless, and a constant source of inspiration.

Opposite page above, Sewing Machine, John J. Greenough, Feb. 21, 1842. The earliest sewing machine invention patented, it was designed with a double pointed needle, an eye in the middle, which passes through the fabric with a running or a backstitch, drawn through by side pincers. The weights draw out the thread, and a stop motion is activated when a thread breaks or is too short. It was made for leather work and other heavy materials, and an awl pierces the hole for the needle to penetrate. The needle takes only short lengths of thread at a time, and frequent rethreading is necessary. This machine was never reproduced and seems to have been Greenough's sole attempt as inventor. Patent No. 2466.

Below left, Sewing Machine, Elias Howe, Boston, Mass., Sept. 10, 1846. This model presented a solution for imitating the movements of the human hand by combining the action of two needles on opposite sides of the fabric and, most revolutionary of all, with the needle holes in their points. Patent No. 4750.

Elias Howe

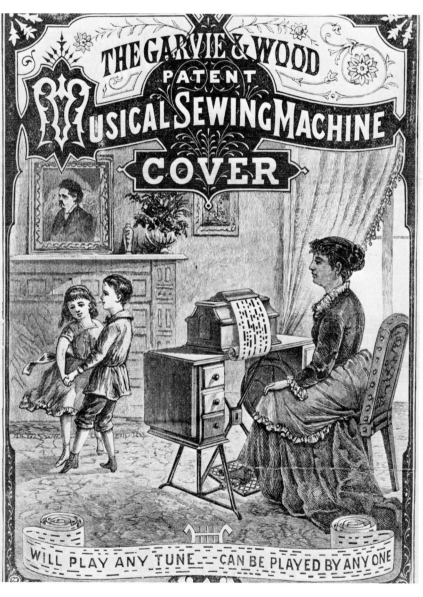

Sewing Machine, Isaac Singer, Oswego, N.Y., August 12, 1851. Machines were already in production when the patent was pending, and this model has serial number 22. The prototype was intended for industrial rather than home use, and is very heavy. It has a presser foot which holds the material to be sewn, on a table, makes a lockstitch with a straight, eye-pointed needle, and draws the stitch tight with a reciprocating shuttle. Between 1851 and 1865 Singer patented nearly 20 improvements, including the yielding presser foot and a continuous wheel feed. Patent No. 8,294.

Improved Hand Spinning Machine, C. Matheny, Greens-
burgh, Ind., Nov. 16, 1869. The spindle carriage, guide track,
and bell crank, are connected to and operated by the treadle, for increased efficiency. Patent No. 96,937.

James Morrison & Co. advertised this fan-
ning attachment for the sewing machine in
the 1870's. Many such devices were available to the seamstress during the time. Every
major technological advance brings in its
wake a host of additional gadgets, only a
few of them true "improvements."

The message was the same in the advertisements of the 1870's as it is today. The days of slavery at the wash tub were nearing their end for the knowledgeable housewife with an eye on the latest labor-saving appliance.

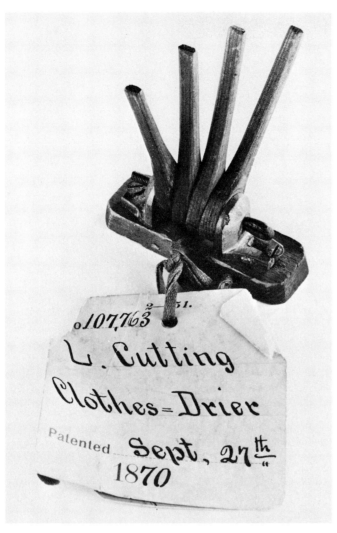

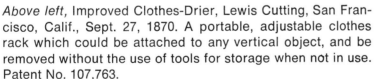

Above left, Improved Clothes-Drier, Lewis Cutting, San Francisco, Calif., Sept. 27, 1870. A portable, adjustable clothes rack which could be attached to any vertical object, and be removed without the use of tools for storage when not in use. Patent No. 107,763.

Above right, Improved Fire Fender or Guard, C. H. Schultz, Cincinnati, Ohio, Nov. 19, 1867. The invention consists of a screen with adjustable hooks, which attaches to the grate, and a small door in the center for attending the fire. Patent No. 71,224.

Below right, Improved Hand Clothes Washer, Peter Falardo, Newark, N.J., and George H. Snow, New Haven, Conn., Feb. 15, 1870. Their invention for wash day is a rubber roller attachment for the corrugated washboard. The clothes could be rolled out and kneaded with this instead of the lady's hands. Patent No. 99,870.

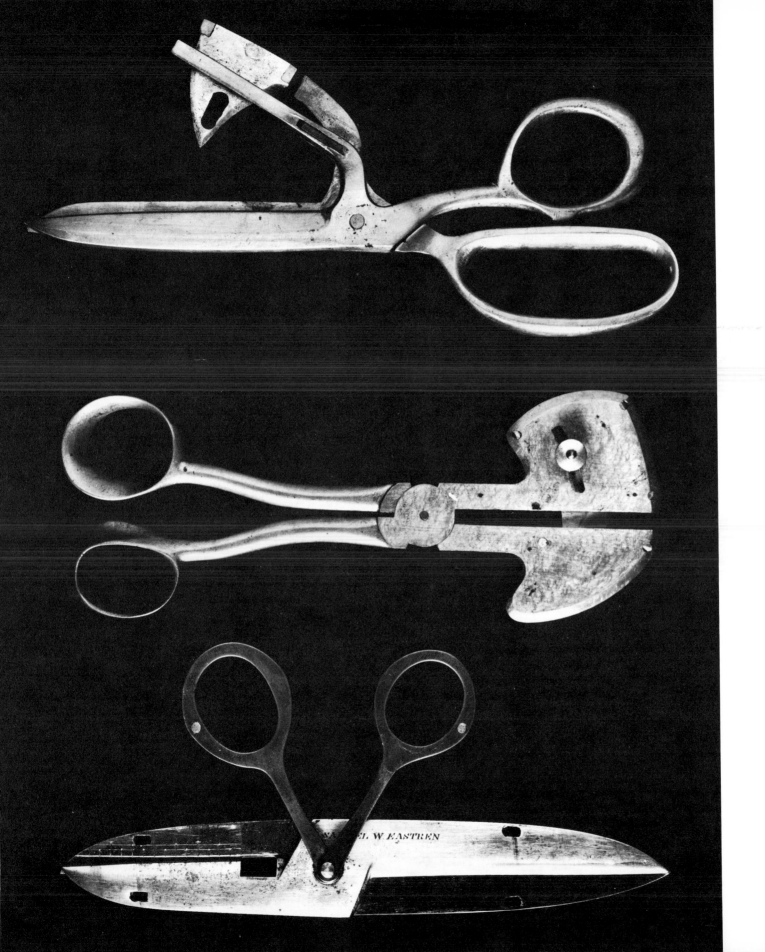

Opposite page, Tailor's Shears, top, Phebe L. Carter and James W. Rhoades, Clyde, Ohio, Apr. 13, 1875, Patent No. 162,029; center, William S. Porter, Boston, Mass., Dec. 15, 1868, Patent No. 84,902. The tailor's shears were intended for use in making button holes of any size and for cutting extra heavy material. The pair below, combination sewing shears and button hole cutter, were made by Samuel Eastern, Tremont, N.Y., July 11, 1871, Patent No. 116,936.

Left, Ventilator, Henry S. Janes, Oshkosh, Wis., Nov. 30, 1869. The regulating device in the elbow of the pipe adjusts the flow of air. It is to be inserted in stove pipes. Patent No. 105,215.

Below, Portable Steam Radiator for Heating Apartments, I. H. Chester, Cincinnati, Ohio, June 30, 1857. The patent application includes the inventor's assurances, based on several months' experience, that four feet of gas will heat an ordinary sized parlor during the five coldest months of the year more healthfully and pleasantly than any other method. The radiator contains a boiler on the bottom and a deflector above for a continuing source of steam heat. Patent No. 17,-666.

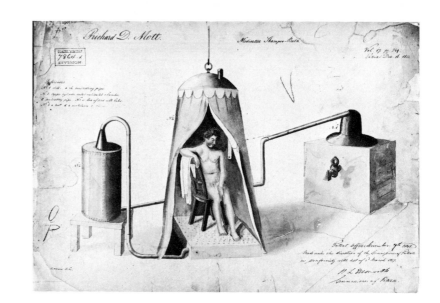

Above, Medicated Shampoo Bath, Richard D. Mott, Dec. 16, 1833. At a time when the daily bath was regarded as unhealthy by the masses, this inventor advocated a medicinal shower to cleanse the scalp. The subject could get his head thoroughly rinsed during the treatment while comfortably seated inside the copper cylinder, termed the medical chamber. Watercolor application drawing by the Patent Office.

Below, Improved Oven, Elisha Graves Otis, Yonkers, N.Y., Aug. 24, 1858. The inventor of the first elevator with an automatic safety device also turned his inventive bent to improving an oven capable of baking many loaves at a time. Baking takes place on a spiral floor with a conveyor belt turning on a rotary cylinder. The temperature is controlled by dampers on a hot air chamber above the fire. Patent No. 21,271.

Improved Boot Tree, Jarvis Howe, June 9, 1874. The front and back are constructed independently of the center piece and may be inserted or removed without removing the main portion of the tree. Patent No. 151,701. Improved Last for Boots and Shoes, Issac F. Williams, Bristol, R.I., Aug. 3, 1875. The instep seam is placed higher on the shoe in order to eliminate drawing and pinching. Patent No. 166,443. Improved Last for Vulcanized Rubber Boots, O. S. S. Squire, North Haven, Conn., July 19, 1859. "Designed for a better, more comfortable wearing shoe, it has been practically tested and found to work successfully." Just how, the inventor does not say. Patent No. 24,830. Straw and Wood Overshoe, F. W. Mitchel, W. C. Wilcox, H. J. Miller, Utica, N.Y., June 1, 1858. One way of keeping feet dry before the advent of rubber boots. Patent No. 20,439.

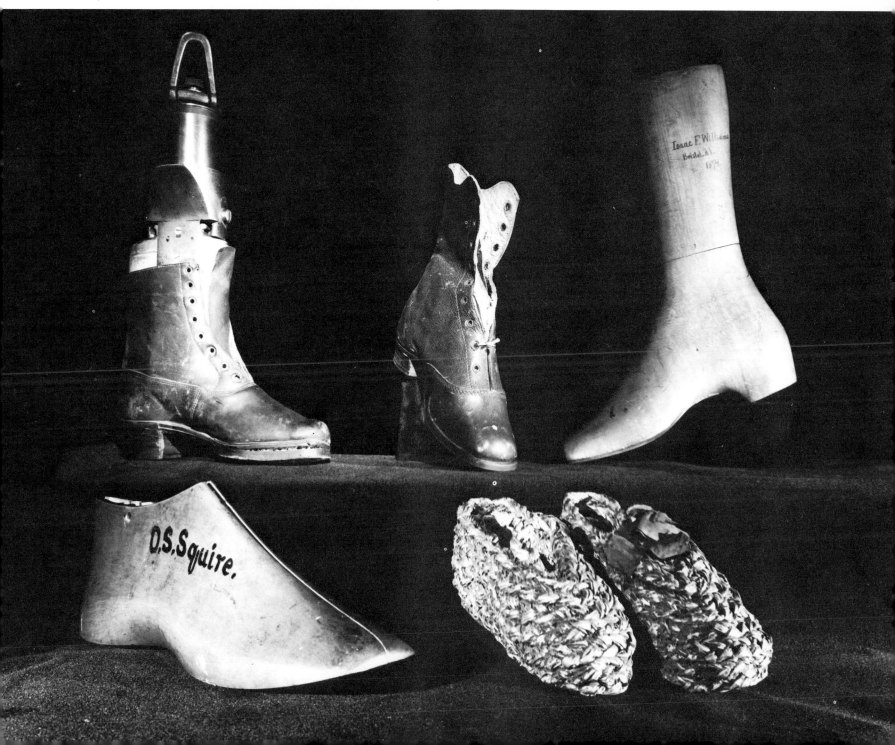

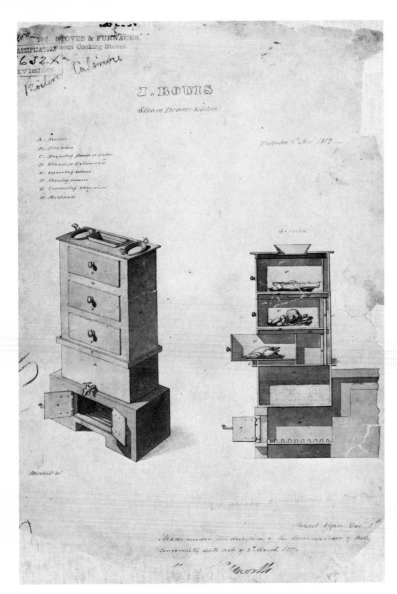

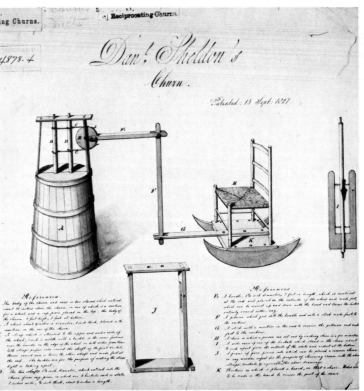

Above left, Steam Drawer Kitchen, John Bouis, Baltimore, Md., Jan. 4, 1812. Bouis also later patented an improved form of metal roofing. His very practical metal chest of drawers contain steam compartments which are heated by a bottom fire. Pipes carry the steam up to the drawers. Watercolor application drawing by the Patent Office.

Below right, Churn and Rocking Chair, Daniel Sheldon, Pultney, N.Y., Sept. 13, 1827. Another labor and time-saving device, one with which the housewife could churn the butter and rock the baby at the same time. The early American inventor relished such opportunities to produce two-in-one, or even three-in-one, contraptions.

46

Above left, Improved Wash-Board, Bertha Kaufman, Philadelphia, Penn., Aug. 13, 1878. The voice of experience was asserting itself when Bertha wrote: "It is well known that in washing with the ordinary wash-board the bending forward is very hard on the breast, especially when the operation is continued for several hours." Therefore, her invention was intended to give relief with a concave cushioned breast rest which would ease the pressure. It could be attached to any ordinary washboard with straps. Patent No. 206,881.

Left, An Improved Combination Stepladder and Ironing Board, Henry and Edward Shanahan, South Bend, Ind., Nov. 11, 1878. Although they knew such a combination had already been presented to the public, the Shanahan brothers improved the frames and pivoting parts which hooked to secure the ironing table, and formed the feet for the base of the ladder. All this was designed to simplify a two-fold device which could be handily stored. Patent No. 215,171.

Right, Improved Snow Shovel, Charles A. Way, North Charlestown, N.H., Oct. 31, 1881. The object of this invention was to produce greater strength and durability through the addition of a metallic clasp which fastened the handle to the blade. The clasp fits over the lower end of the handle and is attached to the blade with bolts. Patent No. 252,822.

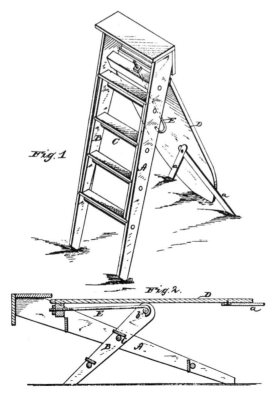

H. C. & E. L. SHANAHAN.
Combined Step-Ladder and Ironing-Table.

No. 215,171.   Patented May 6, 1879.

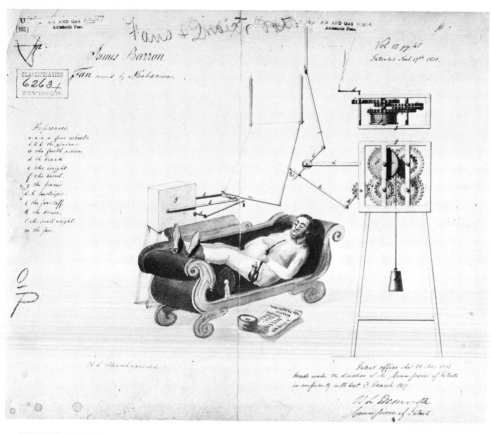

Above, Fan Moved by Mechanism, James Barron, Norfolk, Va., Nov. 27, 1830. Using clock work movements with a winding wheel and weight, the inventor produced a backward and forward movement to keep his fan in motion. Watercolor application drawing by the Patent Office.

Below, Tin, Copper and Zinc Roofs, John Bouis, Baltimore, Md., June 26, 1835. Typical of the application sketches of the time, this drawing is particularly detailed with the landscape fully filled in. Both the apparatus for preparing the roofing and the dwelling for which it is intended is indicated. Watercolor application drawing by the Patent Office.

Q. S. BACKUS.
COMBINED BEDSTEAD AND FIRE PLACE.
No. 334,504.   Patented Jan. 19, 1886.

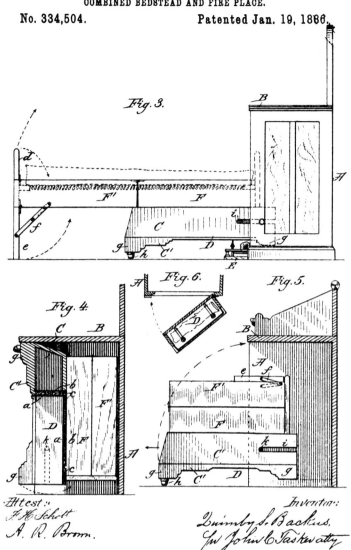

Combined Bedstead and Fireplace, Quimby S. Backus, Winchendon, Mass., Jan. 19, 1886. An unusual contraption designed for small bedrooms, especially those in boarding houses, too small for fireplaces and ordinary furniture. The hearth, with its andirons and log, may be detached from the fireplace and will remain stationary on the floor regardless of the position of the bed. When the fireplace is turned down, the gas or oil log may be extinguished or not, as desired, since the bed is lined with metal and asbestos to prevent any accident by fire. The fireplace can also be combined with a sideboard, wash stand, or wardrobe. Patent No. 334,504.

Right, Fire Ladder, James Johnson, Baltimore, Md., April 18, 1831. The invention includes a series of stairways built on wheels which can be drawn up to the necessary height of a burning building. Its practical application is most visibly rendered. Watercolor application drawing by the Patent Office.

VI. Revolution in Arms

The legend of the frontier rifleman's skill was not a figment of the imagination. Thanks to the inventiveness of early American gunmakers, the frontiersman could be equipped with the best in firearms. German and Swiss gunsmiths who migrated to southeastern Pennsylvania were responsible for improvements made on the rifle in the mid-eighteenth century. It was they who produced the Pennsylvania, and later, the Kentucky rifle, also known as the squirrel gun because of its accuracy in hitting small moving targets. With the Revolutionary War, further improvements in firearms were necessary and quick in coming.

Young men were equipped for battle. The carrying of a gun was a common practice throughout the Colonies. In Georgia, the commonwealth fined any man attending church service without a gun or pistol equipped with at least six charges of powder and ball, ready for firing. The constant threat of surprise Indian attack warranted such precaution. By 1775 the Colonies' forges were already producing over 30,000 tons of iron, most of it for export, and with the outbreak of war this was immediately put to use for the patriotic cause. Many gunsmiths set up the beginnings of factories with three or four-barrel forges, several forges for locks, water mills for grinding and polishing, a foundry for mountings, and numerous skilled workmen perfecting one part of the firearm.

Heavy expenditures, private and public, for arms did not diminish with the end of war. In 1798 Eli Whitney secured a government contract to produce 10,000 muskets using the interchangeable parts method. The system was pioneered as early as 1785 in France by a gunsmith known only as Le Blanc. In an often quoted letter, Thomas Jefferson described meeting the inventor, and assembling several muskets from assorted parts. But it was Whitney who first manufactured a standardized weapon in America from his plant which started production in 1800. It took two years to make the machines, jigs and templates for the factory.

Parts were cast from metal molds, and after being filed, were interchangeable. The volume of guns assembled was steadily increased. The single highly skilled gunsmith who assembled all the parts of a gun was replaced by a number of assembly line workers. By 1810 over 140 factories were producing more than 40,000 firearms. A decade later, the method was the predominant way of manufacture in all armories.

One of the earliest forms of the pistol to gain in popularity during the early nineteenth century was the "pepper-pot" or "pepper-box." Apparently named because it roughly resembled a pepper shaker, it was a pistol with six or more barrels forming a solid piece which either revolved on a central axis, or had a revolving hammer. The first American patent for this type of pistol was granted to Benjamin and Barton Darling in 1836. When Ethan Allen (*not* the Revolutionary War hero) patented a similar model with a double-action lock in the following year, the pepper-box became the fastest firing handgun in the world. It was loaded and primed in advance, and could be drawn and fired in a single motion. The pepper-box was more popular than the Colt revolver for more than a decade. The most famous and popular model was that patented by Christian Sharps, and was a four-barreled version with a revolving firing pin. Over 129,000 of these were produced as late as 1874.

Among other solutions for a multi-firing weapon was the harmonica type gun, with barrels placed side by side, moving in front of the striking mechanism with each shot. The Jarré was widely used in Europe, but was less known in America. The H. S. Josselyn chair revolver, although not a practical design, was one of several inventions patented which illustrate future possibilities for development. Another such weapon was the "organ" gun manufactured by a Rochester, New York, foundry in 1861. It had twenty-five barrels which fired simultaneously, and was first used in the 1864 attack on Fort Sumter. This unwieldy instrument was eventually

Opposite page, Colt-Paterson Revolver, Samuel Colt, Paterson, N.J., Feb. 25, 1836. The model illustrated here was struck especially to replace the original Colt model destroyed in the 1836 Patent Office fire. Although Colt held several patents, this is certainly his most famous. The revolver is .36 caliber, single action, octagonal, with a rifled 8¾" barrel, six chambers, a revolving cylinder, folding trigger, and percussion cap nipples set straight in recesses in the end of the cylinder. Examined closely, you can see the outlines of a scene of a stagecoach hold-up etched on the cylinder. The revolver was made by the Paterson Arms Manufacturing Co. Patent No. 138.

replaced by the Gatling machine gun, invented in 1862 by Richard Gatling of North Carolina. It gained particular notoriety during the last quarter of the nineteenth century in the battlefields of Africa, China, Japan, Turkey and Russia.

Samuel Colt, born in Hartford, Connecticut, in 1814, gained greater fame than any other American armsmaker. While Colt did not claim to have created the multi-firing rotating, cylinder-type firearm, he was the first to make a commercially successful and effective repeating pistol.

While a young man he had been fascinated by guns and explosives. After trying several schools and trade, he was sent in August, 1830 at age sixteen on a brig, the "Corlo," from Boston to Calcutta, as an apprentice seaman. It was during this trip that he saw a revolving pistol made by a fellow New Englander, Elisha Collier, in 1818. Colt thought he could simplify the mechanism, and whittled a pattern of his model. Upon returning to the United States, he convinced his father to have some samples made, but due to the inferior work of the mechanic, the first one blew up and the other didn't fire at all. Fortunately, no one was hurt because Colt had so little confidence in the samples that he set them in a vise and pulled the trigger with a long cord.

To obtain money for further mechanical work by another gunsmith, Colt toured the countryside as "Dr. Coult," demonstrating with great flair the effects of laughing gas. At last he was able to afford the work of a skilled artisan, and in 1835 secured a British patent with his model. An American patent for the same revolver was issued on February 25, 1836.

Colt next attempted to obtain government contracts for a supply of his revolvers to be used by the Texas Rangers during their war with Mexico. During an ambush by the Mexicans, the only survivor was one Captain Thornton, who shot his way out with his Colt revolvers. The account of the escape convinced General Zachary Taylor that this was the gun needed, and at the outbreak of the Mexican-American War in 1846, Colt was given an order for 1,000 revolvers. Unfortunately, the order arrived a year after Colt's first manufacturing facility, a plant in Paterson, New Jersey, had been sold at foreclosure and dismantled. The inventor redesigned his revolver and had patterns made. He took them to Eli Whitney, Jr.'s factory in Whitneyville, Conn., and presented them with the government order. Meanwhile, he began setting up his own firm, the Colt Patent Firearms Company, in Hartford which was ready for production in 1848. Here he prospered by utilizing assembly-line, interchangeable parts, and filling orders from Russia, Turkey and several European governments, as well as from across the expanding United States.

Traction Engine, J. E. Praul, with the U.S. Navy, Washington, D.C., Sept. 26, 1879, Patent No. 221,354. This steam road carriage is propelled by vibrating push-bars, and is typical of those many inventions which sought to imitate human or animal motion in order to achieve mechanical success. Praul explained in his application that the two pairs of walking legs would simulate the movement of cow-like animals. It is doubtful that this machine was ever manufactured.

Animal Tether, James Upson, Tallmadge, Ohio, June 21, 1870, Patent No. 104,667. Using a horse as model, the invention consists of a moveable tether attached to an adjustable sweep. Remaining taut at all times, it allows the animal to move freely within a certain area without tangling the legs or the neck. The tether may also be moved on rollers, thus allowing a change in the animal's grazing area. **Tricycle Velocipede,** Otto Unzicker, Chicago, Ill., May 13, 1878, Patent No. 204,636. A velocipede for the use of young ladies, it is propelled and steered by the motion given to the tiller by the hands and arms. The legs have no work to perform, a situation considered healthier and more proper for the fair sex. The seat is shaped like a lady's side saddle with a suspended stirrup, and allows the rider the same comfort as that enjoyed on a horse. The result is a velocipede of graceful appearance which would give light but invigorating propulsion to the operator. If desired, the vehicle could easily be modified to accommodate boys.

Self-Measuring Device, Elisha L. Spencer, Millville, Mass., Oct. 1, 1878, Patent No. 208,645. An extraordinary amount of effort went into beautifying this most utilitarian of objects – an oil can. This model represents an improvement in self-measuring devices necessary for delivering specific quantities of oil and other liquids without spilling and with the least amount of handling. Three measuring cans of different capacities are hidden beneath the ornate surface, ready to be filled by a turn of the spigot.

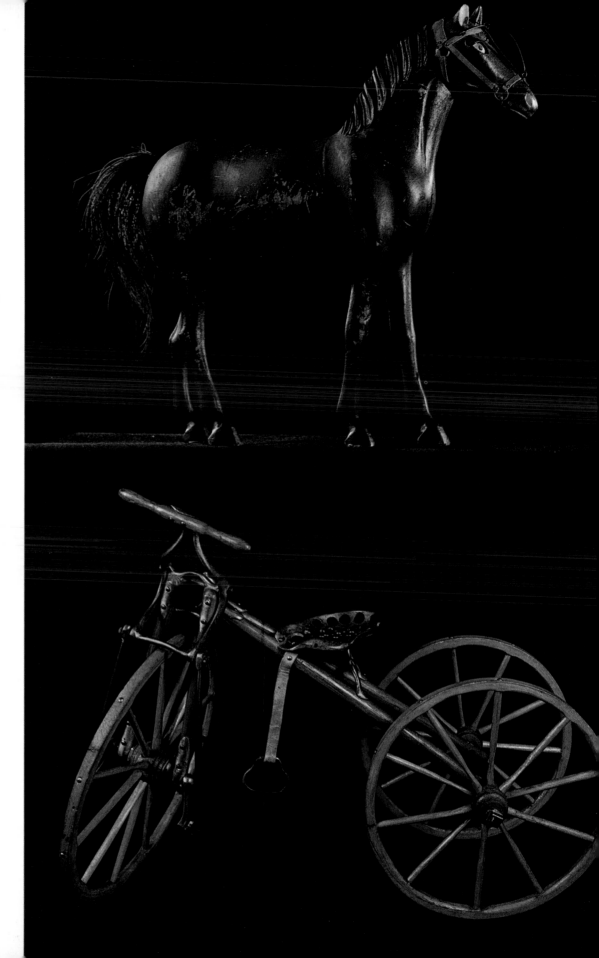

New and Improved Manner of Buoying Vessels Over Shoals, Abraham Lincoln, Springfield, Ill., May 22, 1849, Patent No. 6,469. Lincoln worked on many river boats as a young man and knew the navigating problems encountered with a heavy cargo. His invention called for the use of adjustable, buoyant air chambers which could be attached to a steamboat or other vessel. With their use, the boat would be able to pass over sandbars or through shallow water without unloading its cargo. The chambers were to be connected to the sides of the vessel in such a way that the turning of vertical shafts would expand or contract them. They could be immersed to varying depths by the use of ropes and pullies, and were to be made of waterproof material such as India-rubber cloth.

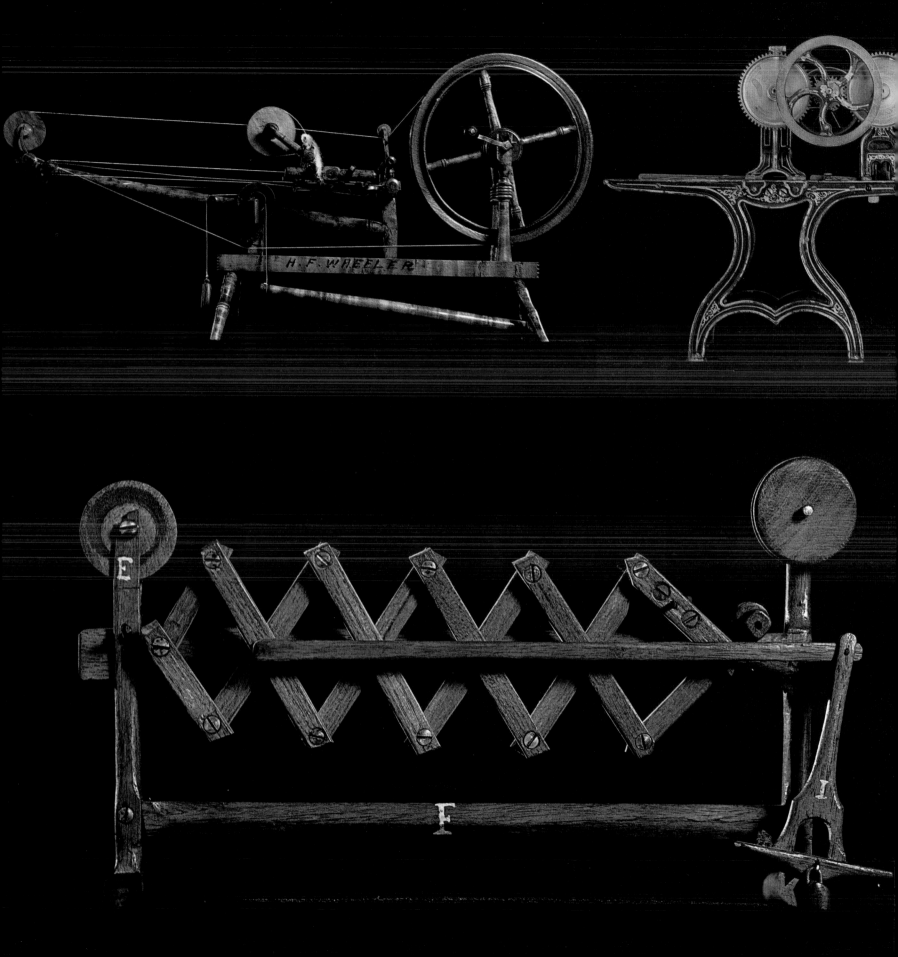

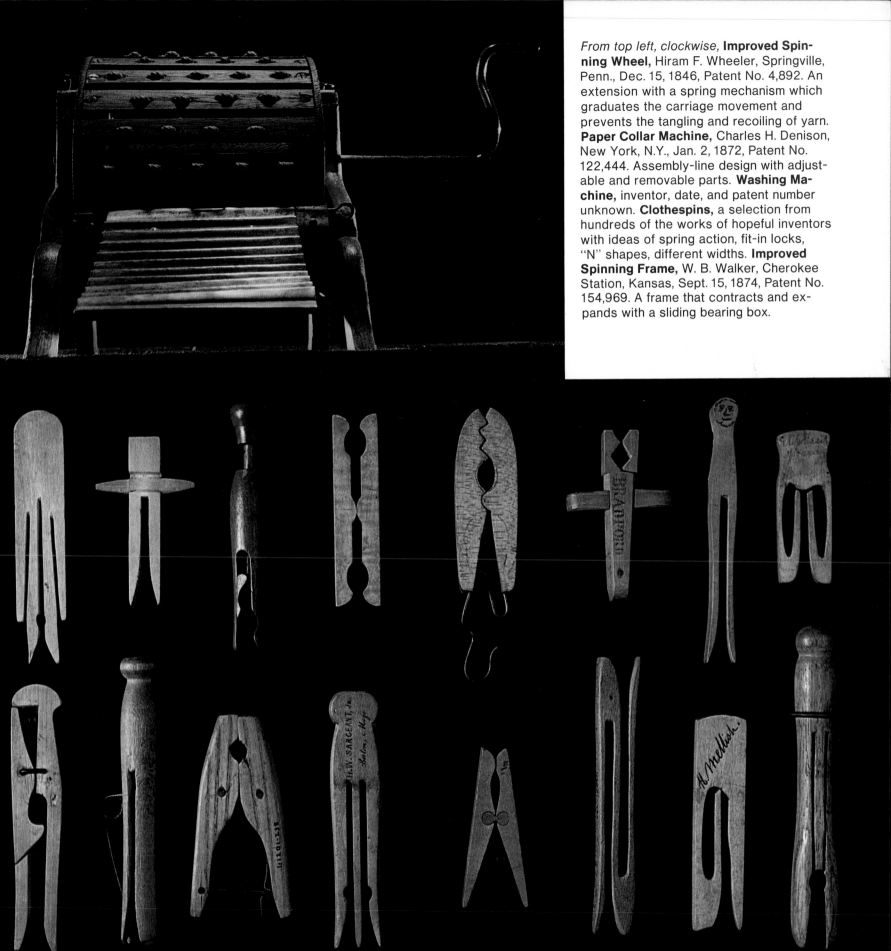

From top left, clockwise, **Improved Spinning Wheel,** Hiram F. Wheeler, Springville, Penn., Dec. 15, 1846, Patent No. 4,892. An extension with a spring mechanism which graduates the carriage movement and prevents the tangling and recoiling of yarn. **Paper Collar Machine,** Charles H. Denison, New York, N.Y., Jan. 2, 1872, Patent No. 122,444. Assembly-line design with adjustable and removable parts. **Washing Machine,** inventor, date, and patent number unknown. **Clothespins,** a selection from hundreds of the works of hopeful inventors with ideas of spring action, fit-in locks, "N" shapes, different widths. **Improved Spinning Frame,** W. B. Walker, Cherokee Station, Kansas, Sept. 15, 1874, Patent No. 154,969. A frame that contracts and expands with a sliding bearing box.

Overleaf, **Mermaid With Attendants Sewing Machine,** W. N. Brown, New York, N.Y., Oct. 25, 1859, Design Patent No. 1,156. A truly decorative and practical machine for the mid-Victorian parlor. Unfortunately, no evidence exists to prove that the model was ever manufactured. The mermaid holds the needle over a serpent presser foot and heart-shape baster plate, while quasi-Roman attendants secure the spool of thread. Several animal designs were patented for the sewing machine, but few were ever produced on a large scale.

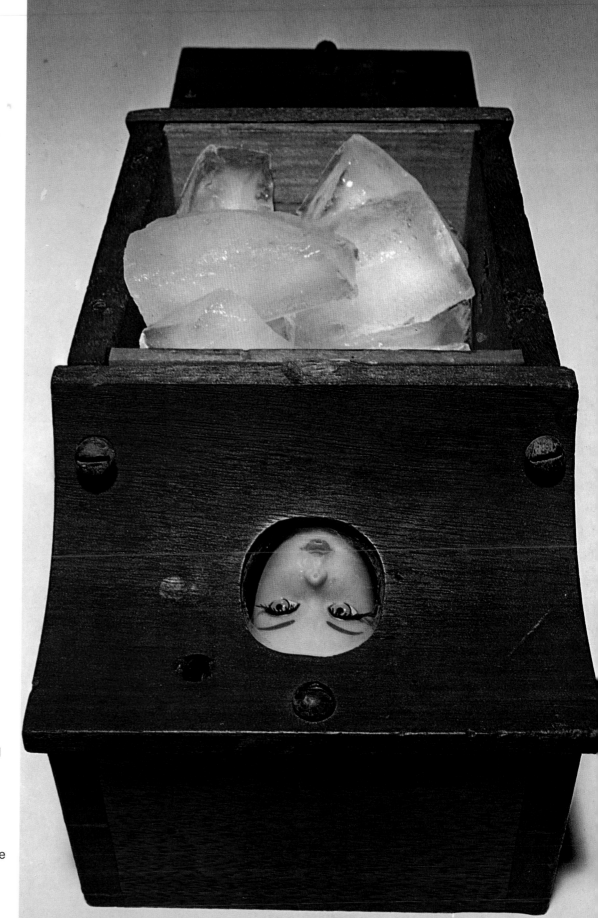

Improved Cherrystoner, William Weaver, Phoenixville, Penn., May 15, 1866, Patent No. 54,797. This contraption, consisting of a disk with ribs on both sides, is connected to a double hopper and could process cherries in double time. **Corpse Preserver,** J. J. Reicherts, Delaware, Ohio, Sept. 29, 1868, Patent No. 82,552. Air conditioned by means of ice compartments with perforations to allow free circulation, a body could be maintained in a composed state for some time. Double walls were filled with charcoal in between for insulation.

At left, **Vegetable Sorter,** John H. Heinz, Sharpsburg, Penn., April 8, 1878, Patent No. 212,000. Vegetables and fruits could be sorted rapidly and efficiently for purposes of preservation, or the produce market. By turning a crank, the contents would have a steady forward and downward movement until they fell from the lower end of the cylinders to the appropriate sized hoppers below. *Below,* **Flailing Machine.** An unknown invention from an equally obscure inventor. The model is one of several made by the Patent Office for the 1893 Chicago Exposition. *At right,* **Drying Kiln,** B. R. Hawley, Normal, Ill., Nov. 17, 1868, Patent No. 84,117. The inventor left no doubt about his "authorship." The clearly marked structure is a drying house, or kiln, to be used for preparing fruit, grain, lumber or clothing. It employs a fire box, enclosed by a hot-air chamber, smoketubes which draw the smoke directly to the two chimneys, and drying chambers equipped with shelves.

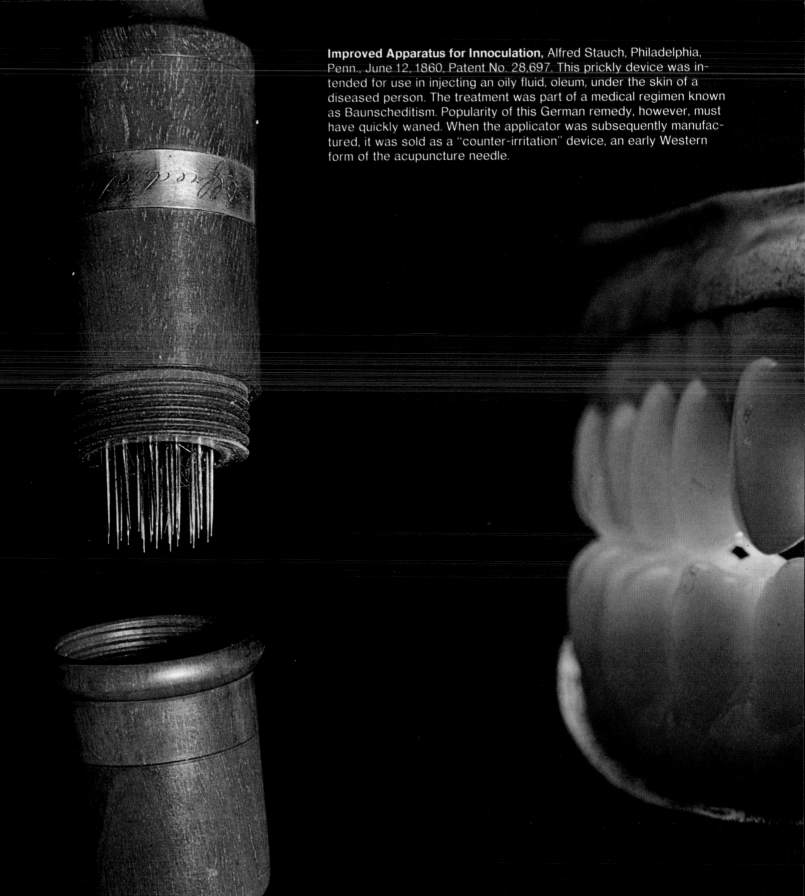

Improved Apparatus for Innoculation, Alfred Stauch, Philadelphia, Penn., June 12, 1860, Patent No. 28,697. This prickly device was intended for use in injecting an oily fluid, oleum, under the skin of a diseased person. The treatment was part of a medical regimen known as Baunscheditism. Popularity of this German remedy, however, must have quickly waned. When the applicator was subsequently manufactured, it was sold as a "counter-irritation" device, an early Western form of the acupuncture needle.

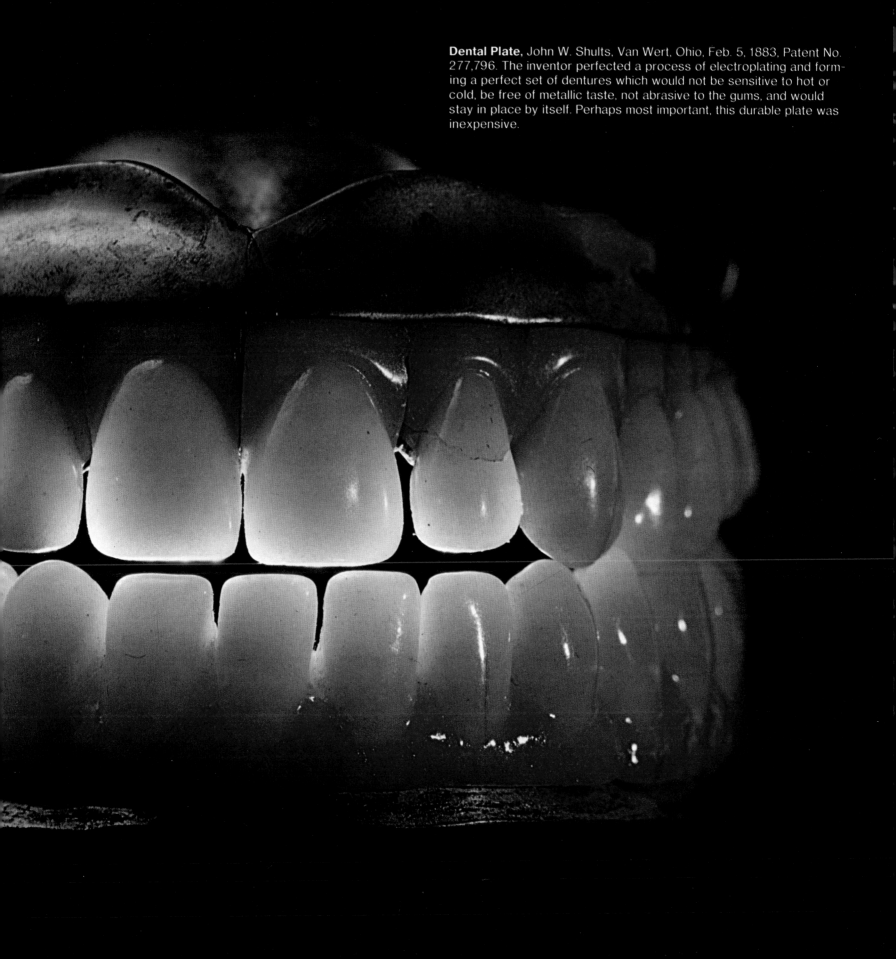

Dental Plate, John W. Shults, Van Wert, Ohio, Feb. 5, 1883, Patent No. 277,796. The inventor perfected a process of electroplating and forming a perfect set of dentures which would not be sensitive to hot or cold, be free of metallic taste, not abrasive to the gums, and would stay in place by itself. Perhaps most important, this durable plate was inexpensive.

Below, **Animal Trap,** John and William Morris, Seward, Nebr., Mar. 18, 1878, Patent No. 203,361. The Morris brothers were only two of the many thousands of American inventors who expected the world to beat a path to their door. Their most perfect mouse or other animal trap combines duplex hinged gates, lips which are operated automatically by a weight thrown down on one of them. Attracted by bait, the creature would pass the lips and enter the jaw. There his weight would trigger a lever closing the mouth. Once inside, the animal would attempt to escape through a second compartment alongside the first. When this second body was entered, its own gate would spring shut. The mouth would then reopen and the trap was set for its next unwary victim.

Above, Samuel Colt with the revolver which has been given credit for winning the West. While Colt did not claim to have created the multi-fire, rotating cylinder-type firearm, he was the first to make a financially successful and truly effective pistol.

The British, master firearms makers, became particularly enamoured of the Colt product and manufacturing method. The American firearms exhibit at London's Crystal Palace in 1851 was certainly as exciting as the agricultural. It included a number of important American-developed rifles by Courtlandt Palmer, and S. E. Robbins and Richard S. Lawrence, and the most popular and acclaimed Colt revolver. The literature for the exhibit described the dangers of the Texas frontier and California trails which were often attacked by Indians. "The ordinary dragoon pistol and Hall's carbine were no match for the daring mounted Indians. Many experienced dragoons have certified that with the aid of a Colt revolver and a Sharps' rifle, even when met with surprise attack in the most vulnerable strategic sites as mountain gorges or on open prairie, they succeeded in scattering an overwhelming number of attackers."

As a result, British industrialists soon came to America to buy machine tools to equip a new armory at Ensfield for the "American system" of manufacturing. The British government lifted its ban on importation of firearms, and orders for Colt revolvers and Marston rifles, in particular, were forthcoming. As for the Exhibition, the American manufacturers were given the only award possible—honorable mention. It was still not fashionable to award prize medals for firearms.

Improved Breech Loading Cannon with Mechanism, A. H. Emery, New York, N.Y., April 11, 1877. Emery perfected a new way of raising the breech lock, tipping the body for loading, closing the breech, and locking the piece into firing position. Heavy cannon casting was greatly improved, out of necessity, during the Civil War, and the technology of warfare continued to develop from that time on. Patent No. 203,020.

"Harmonica" Pistol, Alphonse Etienne Jarré and Pierre Joseph Jarré, Paris, France, Apr. 15, 1873. The model represents an improvement based on an earlier (1862) Jarré patent for the same kind of gun. It is breech loading with a six-rifled barrel which moves laterally into position on the self-cocking hammer's movement. Originally it was one of many designs produced to circumvent Colt's patent. Although widely used in France, it found no market in America. The first such American gun was made by a Utah gunmaker, John Moses Browning, in the 1850's, but he never bothered to patent it. Patent No. 137,927.

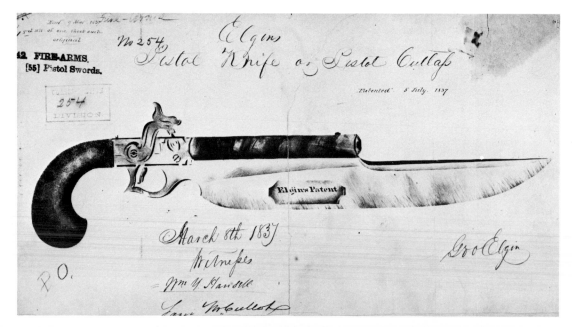

Pistol Knife, George Elgin, New York, N.Y., July 5, 1837. The model, one of the rarest in the Smithsonian patent model gun collection, was made by C. B. Allen, a Springfield, Mass., gun manufacturer who specialized in unusual arms. During the Civil War they were carried as side arms. The weapon is fifty-four caliber, single shot, with the knife trigger guard and hilt all in one piece. Also illustrated is the original application drawing submitted with the model and application form. It would appear from the signature that Elgin himself executed the drawing. Patent No. 254.

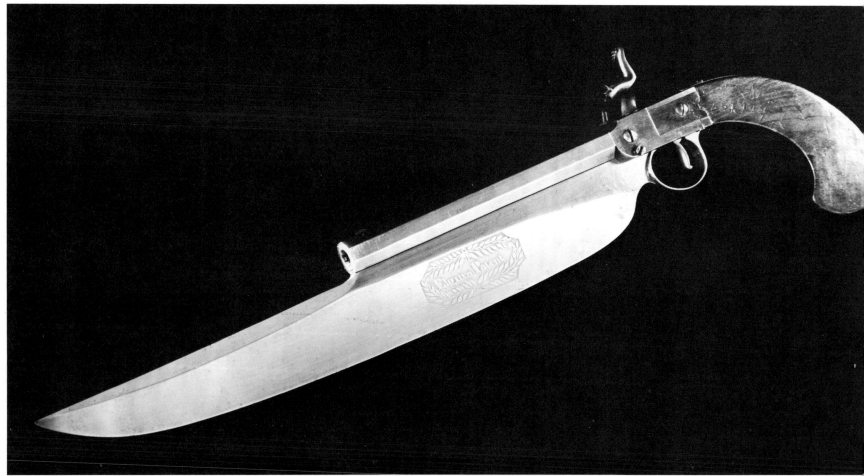

Above, Magazine Pistol, Oliver Percival, East Haddam, Conn., and Asa Smith, New York, N.Y., July 9, 1850. The pistol contains two revolving chambers, one for bullets and the other for powder. It didn't work, despite the grant of the patent. In fact, it was liable to blast off in one's hand. Patent No. 7,496. *Below,* Pepper-box Pistol, George Leonard, Jr., Shrewsbury, Mass., July 9, 1850. Six concentric, stationary, smooth-bored barrels, with a revolving hammer, and a special trigger which will fire the charges successively *and* successfully. Patent No. 7,493.

Below, Revolver, Henry S. Josselyn, Roxbury, Mass., Jan. 23, 1866. This chain pistol, never manufactured, constitutes a unique step in the development of firearms. The barrel is octagonal and is 4½" long. Twenty chambers, 11 1/6" long, are fastened together in a chain which hangs from a revolving ratchet. This is operated by a lock which brings the chamber under the hammer in turn. One of several precursors of the modern machine gun. Patent No. 52,248.

Inverted Channel Wing Aeroplane, Ignatz Glanschnig, Gary, Ind., Nov. 11, 1930. An improvement in design with perfect streamlining, parachute wings, and relatively large, easy rock elevators. The parachute wings are formed with a transverse curvature to facilitate landing in a safe gliding position, and to retard the descent of the ship in the event of engine failure. The novel construction and combination of parts provide a gentle, tapering streamline which is greater than in the conventional type plane, and minimizes air resistance. Patent No. 1,781,455.

VII. Getting There

"Railroad" carriages are pulled at the enormous speed of 15 miles per hour by "engines," which, in addition to endangering life and limb of passengers, roar and snort their way throughout the countryside, setting fire to the crops, scaring the livestock and frightening women and children. The Almighty never intended that people should travel at such breakneck speed.

Respectfully,
Martin Van Buren
Governor of New York

Van Buren might as well have sent his protest of 1829 to the dead letter office. It was intended for President Andrew Jackson, a man who shared the same political sentiments but who, nevertheless, knew that he was as powerless to stop the spread of railroads as Canute had been in halting the movement of waves. At the time, almost all American railroad cars were still being pulled by horsepower; in 1837, the year Van Buren himself became President, there were more than 350 locomotives at work on over 1,450 miles of track.

If many Americans were frightened of speed, countless others were fascinated by it. The first important chapter in American transportation history took place in the original coastal colonies, and, naturally, involved the development of movement over water. During the Revolutionary War there were intermittent experiments with "submarine" vessels, notably David Bushnell's Turtle. This strange contraption, resembling two tortoise shells, was bound together with iron bands and could be submerged for 30 minutes at a time. As an instrument of war it was a bust, but as George Washington later wrote, "I then thought, and still think that it was an effort of genius, but that too many things were necessary to be combined, to expect much from the issue against an enemy, who are always upon guard."

John Fitch and Robert Fulton were able to combine the proper ingredients for a steam propelled vessel under more peaceful conditions. Fitch was the first to do so. In 1787, he took several delegates of the Constitutional Convention on their first steamboat ride up the Delaware. In 1788, he and his partner, Henry Voight, and two stockholders, successfully navigated a steamboat, the Thornton, the 20 miles from Philadelphia to Burlington, N.J., at a speed of four miles an hour. Fitch was not quite able to dock the boat, nor was he able to return to Philadelphia under steampower, but an important step had been taken. A year later the speed was raised to eight miles an hour. Regular service between Philadelphia and Trenton was inaugurated on a new ship, the Perseverance, but since the passenger cabin could only accommodate seven customers due to the vessel's monstrous engine, the company was a commercial failure. When it was destroyed in a storm, Fitch was unable to build another, and resettled in Bardstown, Kentucky, and there committed suicide in 1798.

Robert Fulton's life was considerably more pleasant. Confusion has arisen over the years, but Fulton himself never claimed to have been the original inventor of the steamboat. He was fortunate in securing the patronage of Robert R. Livingston, a wealthy New York landowner who had obtained a monopoly on steam navigation of the Hudson from New York to Albany, and who financed a 20-horsepower Watt and Boulton engine for the vessel. In 1807 the Clermont made its first successful voyage up the Hudson. Fulton, earlier an accomplished gunsmith and painter, added a private forutne gained from the Hudson River line, to his list of credits. Securing a patent was, however, a more difficult feat.

William Thornton, the first commissioner of patents, had been one of Fitch's early benefactors. Thornton rejected Fulton's early claims for originality on some elements of the steamboat invention, and only relented in 1809 under pressure. That Fulton was an inventive genius, however, can not be denied. He had always been intrigued with improvements in the machinery of naval warfare, and during the War of 1812 resumed work on plans first outlined during the Revolutionary War. Fulton dusted off his drawings for a submarine, the Nautilus, earlier peddled to the French and English, and began designing the world's first steam warship, the Demologos. It was patterned after a ferry boat, with a center paddle wheel, and was the prototype of the Civil War ironclads. Unfortunately, Fulton died of pneumonia in 1815 while overseeing its construction, and the ship was never completed.

Certainly the important key to the development of these inventions, as it would be for the locomotive—was the engine. Great Britain led the world in 1800 in engine production, but the process was still a crude one. Americans were quick to seize an opportunity to excel in this new field. Oliver Evans built his first high-pressure steam engine in 1804, and went into the manufacturing of engines in 1807 at his Mars Iron Works. The legendary Revolutionary hero, Paul Revere, built and improved the boilers for Fulton's later boats.

Credit must be given to Englishman Richard Trevithick for the development of a single cylinder steam locomotive capable of hauling a loaled train. The first locomotive to run in America was made in England, the six-ton *Sturbridge Lion*, for the Delaware and Hudson Railroad. In 1829 it was tested and found too heavy for the track and too high for the bridges. American locomotive builders such as Matthias Baldwin, William Morris, and Peter Cooper created a new national industry. By 1837, of the 350 locomotives at work, only 75 were imported. The addition of cowcatchers and other improvements designed to facilitate movement around curves, laid the groundwork for the emergence of a distinctive American form in locomotive design. John B. Jervis, of the Mohawk and Hudson Railroad, devised the "bogie" truck or swivel which gave a better distribution of weight to his locomotive, the *Experiment*. It had a four-wheeled truck placed under the boiler which was mounted on a pivot which could follow the curves of the track. Eventually, Jervis built a five-foot-long boiler, with four drivers, his bogie truck, and a cowcatcher—a contribution of inventor Isaac Dripps. This form came to be known as the "basket construction."

With such a vast expanse of land to cover, emphasis was first given to speed by rail. The accident rate was appallingly high, not unlike that known today on the superhighway, and remained so until the invention of the coupler, patented by Eli Hamilton Janney in 1868, and the air brake by George Westinghouse in 1869. Standardization of gauges to 4' 8½" (the same as used by Roman chariots), the opening of a transcontinental system in 1869, and the establishment of four time zones (there were over fifty in the 1830's) completed the first important phase of American transportation history. The engineering skill and ingenuity so pragmatically learned in these years was to be richly applied in the last quarter of the nineteenth and first quarter of the twentieth century to, first, the bicycle, then the motor car, and, last, the ultimate in the inventor's dream world, the flying machine.

Sketch of the "Turtle," the first submarine designed for warfare by Connecticut patriot David Bushnell. After several test dives in Long Island Sound, and with the approval of General Washington, Sergeant Ezra Lee was chosen to engineer his solitary submarine attacks on Admiral Howe's British fleet in New York harbor in August, 1776. They failed.

"HONOR TO WHOM HONOR IS DUE"
ORIGIN OF STEAM NAVIGATION.
A VIEW OF COLLECT POND AND ITS VICINITY
in the City of New York in 1793.

On which Pond, the first boat, propelled by Steam with paddle wheels or screw propellers was constructed by John Fitch, six years before Robert Fulton made trial of his boat upon the River Seine, in France, and ten years prior to his putting into opperation his boat Clermont in New York; with a representation of the boat and its machinery, on the Collect pond

BY JOHN HUTCHINGS

Nº 3 Wesley Place, Williamsburgh, L. Island.

1846.

John Fitch's...

as seen on the Delan...

900826A

John Fitch Born in Conn: 21st of June 1743. First we find him a farmers boy, next an apprentice to a Watch-maker, then in a store at Trenton N.J with a stock valued at 3000 doll! all of which was destroyed, when the British took Trenton next a Lieutenant in the A.Army, taken prisoner by the Indians, and sold from one tribe to another through the N.W.Territory, until he was purchased by an Englishman and thus obtained his freedom. During this time he became acquainted with that part of the country of which he made a map, and although printed on a common Cider press it had an extensive sale. He was then a Surveyor in Kentucky, then a Civil Engineer in Pª and on the Delaware made his first experiment of a Steam-Boat with Paddles, he then left America, and traveled through France and England, but not meeting with the encouragement anticipated, became poor and returned home, working his passage as a common sailor to Boston, from there to his native town in Connecticut, thence to New York, where he remained some time, then back to Kentucky where he died in 1798.

Mr John Hutchings
Sir

I have a perfect recollection of having seen a Boat on the Collect Pond in this City with a screw Propeller in the Stern driven by Steam across the Pond. I do not recollect the year but I am certain that it was as early as 1796, it was about the size of a Ships yawl.

New York, July 3d 1846.

I am Sir Respectfully
yours &c.

Anthony Lamb

Residence, Albion Place
City N.York.

This is to Certify, that we have Personally known Mr John Hutchings of the Village of Williamsburg for the last Forty years past, and have the utmost confidence in him for truth & veracity
New York, Octr 10th 1846.

Richard Leayworth

Abott O. Halsted

Residence 178 Franklin st. City N.Y. was a member of the first Methodist Class in the City of N.Y. and has been a Respectable member of the M.E. Church from its commencement in the U.S.

Senior Partner of the Firm of Halsted, Hains & Co. Nº 31 Nassau St.N.Y. Family Residence Orange N.Jersey.

New York, July 3rd 1846.

To Mr John Hutchings
Dear Sir,

It affords me much pleasure, to state that I was an eye witness to the circumstance of a Boat, being propelled by Steam on the Collect Pond in this City about the Year 1796 as exhibited on your Map and that I have a perfect recollection of all these Localities as there shewn, and you are perfectly welcome to use my name in connection with it.

Yours
Wm H. Mustook
City Surveyor

State of New York
City and County of New York Sſ

John Hutchings of Williamsburgh L.I.being duly Sworn deposeth and saith that the facts set forth in the foregoing remarks and description by him, subscribed are correct to the best of this deponents remembrance and belief

Sworn before me, this First day of December 1846.

John Hutchings

Thomas S Henry
Com. of Deeds &c.

S. S. 1797. 8 When his health would allow of moderate exercise, he wrought upon a model Boat about three feet in length, at the shop of Mr Howell Its machinery was constructed of brass. This model Boat had wheels, and has been seen floating in a small stream near the Village by persons now living. It was burnt in Mr Cown's tavern in 1805 Nelson Cº Kentucky

(Sparks American Biography)
New Series Vol. VI.

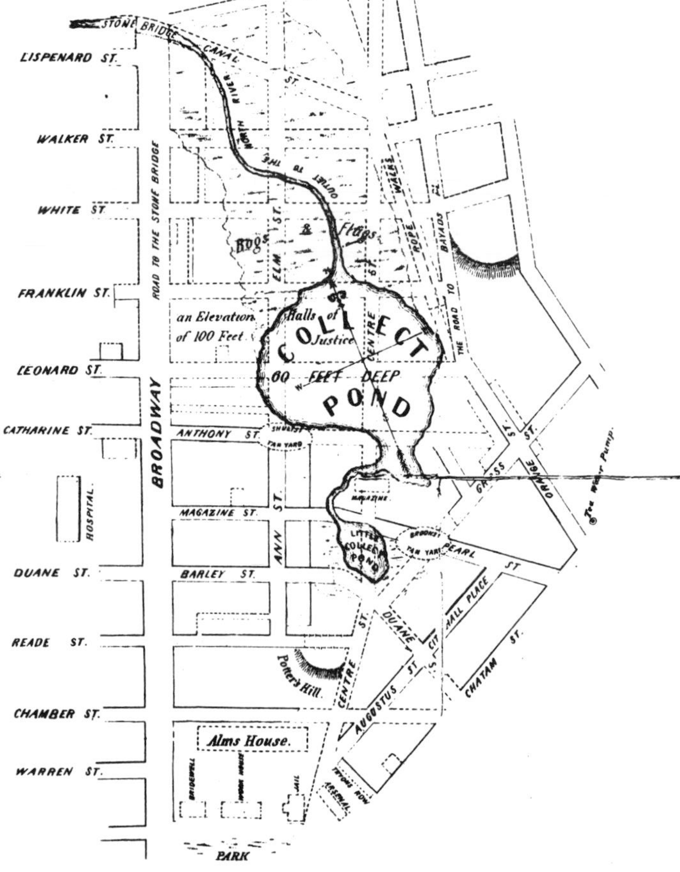

REMARKS. In the S...
Mr Fitch in steering the bo...
Machinery. At that time Rob...
Fitch and the lad Hutching...
pond on different occasions, ...
Modus Operandi of the Mach...
from the State of N.Y. I beli...
application of steam to boats ...
represented in the drawing (do...
Robert Fulton. I being a lad h...
believe Colonel Stevens of th...
Rosevelt had some knowledg...
In conversation Mr Fitch rem...
wheels splashed too much an...
that time, thought of having...
boat might be propelled 6 M...
The steam was sufficiently hig...
pond, when more water bein...
She was again ready to star...

DESCRIPTION. The bo...
length and 6 ft. beam, with ...
steered at the bow with a ...

The boil...
firmly fastened to it by an i...
barrel shaped on the outside,...
steam pipe led directly from ...
or valve box. The leading p...
cylinder F and longer one ...
to the extremities of the work...
the connecting rod was so a...
passed horrizontally through...
propeller or screw as at ...
attached likewise to the wor...
refference to the attached p...

A. Boiler. ...
E dº G, Supporter of beam. ...
Nº L Mr Fitch, 2, Mr Fulton, 3 ...

The boat, t...
by Mr Fitch, and left to deca...
away piece by piece by the chil...
Fitch left New York for Kentu...
troubles Having made his la...
enterprise of Steam Navigat...

John Fitc...
R. Fulton had written their o...
them would have left some a...
but finding no account of it ...
account of it as I possibly can...
to be perfectly correct. If his p...
have been blessed with Steam ...

The progress of Steam Navig...
nearly all Navigable waters on the...
Fitch's prediction in a letter to F...

Charles Brownne built the Clern...
came from England. James P.Allan...
for Steam boats, did the brass w...
on board the boat and Fulton w...
that was with us on the Collec...
Hook & made in speed from 4 t...

Census of the City New York Periods

Periods	
1697	4305
1699	6000
1756	13040
1771	21465
1790	33231
1800	60008
1810	96313
1820	123000
1825	166000
1830	203005
1835	269873
1840	312710
1844	371702

The Model Boat. at Bardstown, 1797-8.

THE WORLD IS INDEBTED FOR THE ORIGINAL IDEA AND TO THE MECHANICAL GENIUS OF JOHN FITCH, OF EAST WINDSOR, CONN.

And to the perseverance and indefatigable attention to the use of Steam of Robert Fulton Esq. Pª The wealth & exalted character of Robert R. Livingston Esq Chancellor

Entered according to act of Congress in the year 1846 by JOHN HUTCHINGS in the Clerk's Office of the District Court of the Southern District of N.Y

Map labels: STONE BRIDGE, LISPENARD ST., WALKER ST., WHITE ST., FRANKLIN ST., LEONARD ST., CATHARINE ST., DUANE ST., READE ST., CHAMBER ST., WARREN ST., BROADWAY, CANAL, RIVER, STONE BRIDGE, CENTRE ST., BAYARD, ELM ST., COLLECT POND, 60 FEET DEEP, an Elevation of 100 Feet, Halls of Justice, ANTHONY ST., MAGAZINE ST., BARLEY ST., ANN ST., PEARL ST., Powers Hill, LITTLE COLLECT POND, Alms House, PARK, HOSPITAL, ROAD TO THE STONE BRIDGE, THE ROAD TO BAYARD

Above, Portrait of John Fitch. Of all inventors in America, he suffered the most ignominious fate. Even today less known than Fulton, it was not until 1926 that Congress appropriated a sum of money for the erection of a monument celebrating Fitchs' genius and, in particular, the invention of the steamboat.

everance

d 7 miles an hour.

*7 M: Hutchings, then a lad, assisted
attending to the working of the
Esq. and Robert Fulton with M:
assed several times around the
plained to Livingston & Fulton the
having a patent for his invention
ave been the original inventor of the
ower and likewise, the two persons
been Robert R. Livingston Esq. and
only with M: Fitch. From hearsay, I
and another person by the name of
ise, and felt an interest in its success.
m that in a former experiment paddle
sed in Canal Navigation. No one in
to: boxes. They had no doubt, but the
ugh then making something less,)
oat once, twice or thrice around the
the boiler (: r pot) and Steam generated
edition —*

*m long boat, or Yawl about 18 ft. in
d round bows, with seats. She was
he propeller was used.
allon iron pot, with a lid of thick plank
ansversly. The Cylinders were of wood
e inside, strongly hooped. The main
a copper box, (about 6 inches square) received
into the bottom or base (The one short
ers and each piston rod was attached
eam was supported by an iron upright,
the crank of the propelling shaft which
boat and was made fast to the
worked by a simple contrivance
ill be easily seen and understood by
gs.*

*ive box. D, Smoke pipe. E, Cylinder
, valve rod. K, Crank. L, Screw propeller.
Esq. i, Lad Hutchings.*

*ortion of its machinery was abandoned.
re of the Collect Pond and was carried
hbourhood for fuel. In the Autumn M:
to go by his pecuniary and domestic
ort, to succeed in this glorious*

*in the year 1798, and if he or
ve no doubt, either one or both of
ransaction as related here by me,
either, I have given as exact an
oken of it, I do believe my memory
ished. J Fitch the means, we should
r fifteen years sooner than we were*

Hutchings

*date to the present period is such that
have Steam boats on them, thus fulfilling
12ª 1785.*

*on & Fulton in 1806 and the machinery
nd has been manufacturing machinery
York for the Boat, as I was repeatedly
then believed him to be the same man
he Clermont left the wharf at Corlears
r 1807.*

of New York. **900826A**

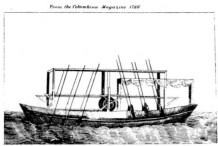

Plan of Mr Fitch's Steamboat

Opposite, Robert Fulton's drawing for a device to be used in sending a message from a submerged vessel to a boat above. The message was to be written on parchment, rolled up, and placed inside a piece of cork. When released, it would float to the surface, attached to a silk line suspended from the boat. Presumably, it could also be wound back down for a response.

I have given my Country a most Valuable Discovery on the 30 of August 1785, for which I have received no Compensation, and I doubt not but common justice will induce them to do something for me, especially when they can do it for the benefit of our Empire ———

Another inducement which urges me to pursue this scheme is, to put it out of the power of future Generations to make excuses for the present one — And if I should die in penury, want, wretchedness and Rags, that my country may have no excuse; and that I may have the secret pleasure, in the Contemplation of receiving real pitty from future Generations.

all which is humbly submitted to the Company
By
John Fitch

25 Decm. 1790

Excerpt from Fitch autobiography manuscript. Written in 1790 at the urging of a sympathetic friend, it provided Fitch with an opportunity to set down all the injustices he had encountered. Above the excerpt is the 1786 drawing sent to the editors of the *Columbian Magazine* with a description of his steamboat. It had two sets of six canoe paddles, which alternately made eleven-foot strokes with each evolution.

Map of the Great Lakes Region by John Fitch, 1785. The inventor, assuredly an accomplished cartographer, drew the map to earn money for his steamboat experiments. He also engraved the plate and printed 600 copies on a cider press in Warminster, Bucks County, Penn. It is one of the first maps to indicate the Canadian boundary as delineated in the Treaty of Paris in 1783, and the territories west of Ohio which Congress proposed in 1785.

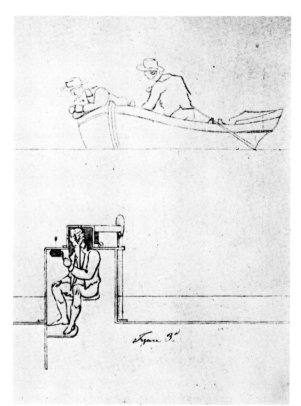

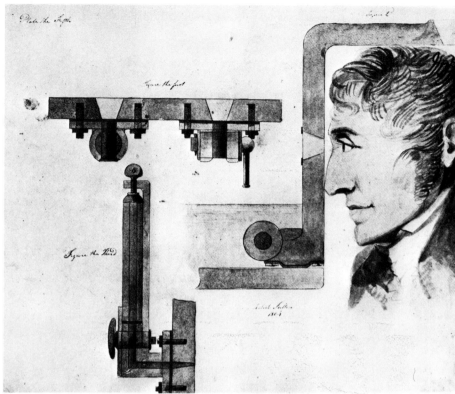

Above right, Robert Fulton as seen in the gyroscope of a submarine vessel. This drawing is one in a series of watercolors by Fulton made during the course of secret negotiations with the British from 1804-1806. He was the first to design a practical, strategic submarine which would accommodate a large crew.

Below right, Drawing of the "Nautilus" by Robert Fulton, a two-man submarine driven by hand cranks. It was successfully submerged in the Seine River in Paris, opposite Les Invalides, for 45 minutes on June 13, 1800. But it was not fit for battle against the British Navy. Napoleon financed the project, much to his regret.

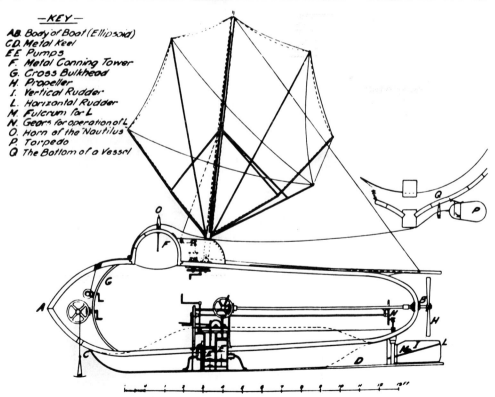

—KEY—

AB. Body of Boat (Ellipsoid)
CD. Metal Keel
EE. Pumps
F. Metal Conning Tower
G. Cross Bulkhead
H. Propeller
I. Vertical Rudder
L. Horizontal Rudder
M. Fulcrum for L
N. Gears for operation of L
O. Horn of the Nautilus
P. Torpedo
Q. The Bottom of a Vessel

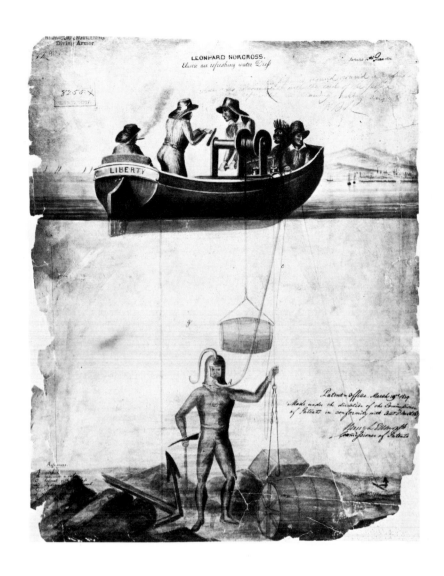

Above left, Elastic Air Refreshing Water Dress, Leonard Norcross, Dixfield, Me., June 14, 1834. The "invention" in action during an underwater treasure hunt, complete with crew, smoking, at the wheel, and in native costume. This was one of many ideas proposed for elastic or India rubber "diving armor" to allow for an air supply to the diver. Watercolor application drawing by the Patent Office.

OLIVER EVANS' ORUKTER AMPHIBOLOS.

Opposite page below, and left, "Oruktor Amphibolos," Oliver Evans' invention, was America's first steam-powered dredger, and was commissioned by the Philadelphia Board of Health in 1805. At the time, Evans took an advertisement in the *Philadelphia Gazette* to announce "steam trials at Center Square." He described his contraption as a "steam engine on board a flat bottomed boat, to work a chain of hooks to break up the ground, with buckets to raise it above water, and deposit it in another boat to be carried off . . . ." The machine was built in Evans' shop, one and a half miles from the river, and although it weighed about 40,000 pounds, he announced his intention of moving it to the water by the power of the engine. "Its first state will then be, a Land Carriage moved by steam." All original drawings have been lost, all that remains is this depiction from *The Mechanic* of July, 1834.

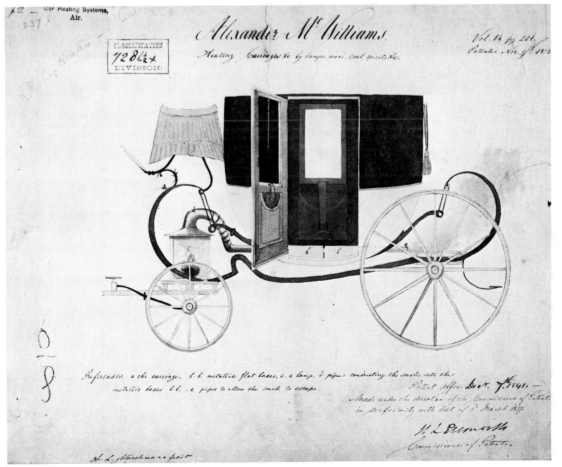

Left, Carriage Heater, Alexander McWilliams, Nov. 9, 1832. McWilliams' improvement was a simple heating lamp which could use coal, oil, or spirit. Heat was conducted through a pipe to metal boxes directly under the floor of the passenger compartment. An exhaust pipe carried the smoke to the rear of the cab. Watercolor application drawing by the Patent Office.

67

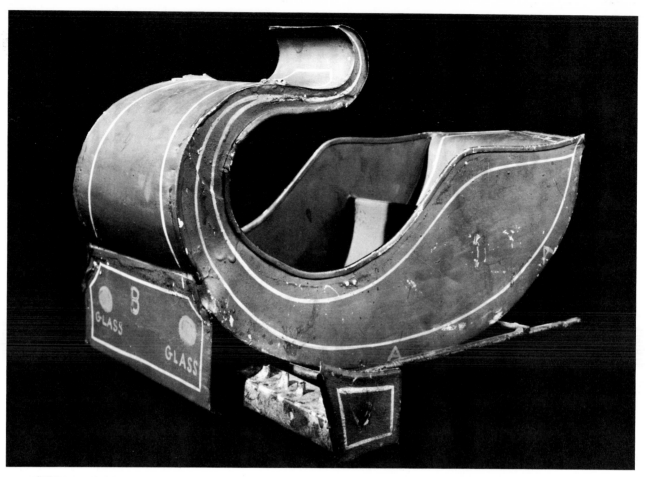

Above, Improved Sleigh Heater, Alfred Norton, Kokomo, Ind., May 2, 1871. Frosty Indiana winters inspired the lamp which would fit the lower front width of the sleigh. It used kerosene for fuel, and was designed to keep the feet the warmest, with the heat rising through the vent under the passenger's seat. Patent No. 114,466.

Opposite, Improved Velocipede, Charles Hammelmann, Buffalo, New York, August 13, 1879. Among many improvements cited by the inventor are the spring under the seat intended to increase the rider's comfort, and a ratchet device attached to the double fork and front wheel which propels the vehicle forward with a "vibrating motion." This ratchet also prevents the vehicle from moving backward, which the inventor felt would make it simpler and less irritating for the beginner. He explained, "in the ordinary course of travel, no backing of the machine is necessary." Patent No. 225,010.

Overleaf, Improved Railroad Engine, Ross Winans, Baltimore, Md., Apr. 27, 1858. Winans presented a new way of constructing, combining and arranging the various parts of the wood-burning engine in order to obtain an enlarged fire-box suitable for burning coal efficiently. The use of coal necessitated a larger fire-box and grate surface. The series of eight driving wheels are in front of the box, and the house for the engineer is placed on the body of the boiler. Patent No. 20,117.

Right, Improved Roller Skate, Lewis B. Jackson, Jr., Philadelphia, Pa., Apr. 2, 1879. With this skate, making a turn or curve is simple. A slight turning of the foot causes the roller to turn inward, and the skater can smoothly execute his maneuver. The front rollers are attached to an axle which turns on a ball, depending on the pressure of the skater's weight. Patent No. 215,-752.

Overleaf, Improved Air Ship, John Cameron, New York, N.Y., Aug. 28, 1878. The object of this invention is an air vessel which can fly horizontally and at any angle, up and down, while carrying passengers and freight. The hollow cylinders are designed to be filled with hydrogen gas, and are connected by a tube to the furnace engine, which raises or lowers the temperature to correspond with the surrounding air. A hydro-carbon engine furnishes the propelling power, with oil for fuel. Patent No. 210,238.

Above, Improved Bicycle, William Klahr, Myerstown, Pa., Mar. 5, 1883. A new manner of propelling the bicycle—a combination of pedals and a ratchet-wheel—and an adjustable saddle mounted on a spring bar. This was one of many improvements patented during the 1870's and 1880's which brought great popularity to the bicycle. Patent No. 285,821.

VIII. Tilling the Soil

History celebrates the battlefields
whereon we met our death, but scorns
the plowed fields whereby we thrive.
—Jean Henri Fabre

The American farmer had to innovate to survive. By the end of the Revolutionary War all the basic farm implements had undergone changes from those heavy Dutch and English models which the early settlers had used. The moldboard of the ordinary plow was made from the wood of a winding tree, hewn with the grain to form its smooth curve. Whenever possible the tip was shod or edged with steel; if not, the farmer improvised with any available metal scraps from worn out horseshoes to old hoe blades.

When Charles Newbold of Philadelphia took out the first American patent for a cast iron plow on June 26, 1797, and tried to interest the public in it, Thomas Jefferson and some of his gentlemen farmer friends expressed enthusiasm. But the average farmer would have nothing to do with the "new-fangled" thing. They said that the iron would poison the land, and encourage the growth of weeds. Newbold spent most of his life and a considerable fortune trying to promote an invention no one would buy. Jethro Wood, of Poplar Ridge, New York, in 1819 was able to break down the resistance to the use of cast iron by introducing inter-changeable parts. His "Improved Plow" was the first to introduce the moldboard shape from which the modern one is based. By the 1830's, the cast iron plow with inter-changeable parts was in general use in the Mid-Atlantic states.

When farmers reached the Midwestern plains, they discovered that iron plows were less successful because the soil stuck to them. Leonard Andrus, the Vermont-born founder of Grand Detour, Illinois, went into partnership with blacksmith John Deere in 1837 to produce the first Grand Detour self-scouring steel plow. The moldboard was made from a broken circular saw from Andrus' sawmill. In 1868 founder James Oliver's chilling method made him one of the most successful plow manufacturers in America. He held several patents for improvements, including a mirror-like finish which was rust resistant, and the "slip-nose" share, which allowed the reversing or replacing of a worn part. By 1878 more than 175,000 Oliver plows were in use.

Both George Washington and Thomas Jefferson invented drills which were used on their farms. But before William T. Pennocks patented a practical grain drill in 1841, the common method of seeding grain was by hand. The methods differed—three or four to a hill and covering with a hoe, the Biblical method of throwing seed to the wind while reciting the rhyme, "One for the blackbird/One for the crow/One for the cutworm/And three to grow." Many unpatented home-made drills were devised, as well as several foot corn planters, and these were used with varying success, depending on the terrain to be covered. By the 1860's and early 1870's the grain drill was in general use in the level wheat country.

In 1857 C. W. Cahoon of Brooklyn, New York, patented a hand-rotation seeding machine guaranteed to sow six acres an hour of a hilly and/or rocky terrain. In the early 1870's the end gate seeder was introduced, with a rotating machine attached to a wagon box and driven by the rear wheel sprocket. George W. Hendrick's invention patented in 1872, which cut a furrow, dropped the seeds and covered the grain, completed the original cycle of invention.

Hand flailing was one of the slowest, most laborious, expensive and wasteful operations done on the farm. By 1833 there were about 700 different kinds of threshing machines on the market, although some models, especially those hand-operated with a crank, required more work than the old method. The first practical threshing machine was invented by Hiram and John Pitt in 1836. It combined threshing, separating and winnowing, and could thresh about 230 bushels a day. Hiram opened a factory in Illinois to serve the Midwest. By the 1850's wheat threshing had become one of the first specialized agricultural businesses in the United States, as it was handled by itinerant operators.

Many inventors were working on the idea of a mechanical harvester when Cyrus McCormick, his father, Robert, and a Negro slave and friend, Jo Anderson, built a "grain cutter" in

Windmill, Jacob Longyear and Daniel W. Clark, Grass Lake, Mich., Dec. 9, 1879. One of man's oldest instruments, it was not a perfect mechanism. This "improvement" consists of a regulating or governing van which, upon reaching a certain velocity, will turn the wheel to put it out of the wind. Patent No. 222, 515.

the blacksmith shop of their Walnut Creek, Virginia, farm in 1831. Many earlier attempts between 1809 and 1816 had been abandoned in frustration by his father, and on July 25, 1831, the machine was ready to be demonstrated. A small crowd of harvesters gathered near Steele's Tavern to watch a boy on a horse pull the reaper through the grain, with Jo Anderson alongside, raking the platform clean, and the young inventor following. The machine cut as much grain as six laborers with scythes, or twenty-four with sickles.

In 1834 Cyrus McCormick was granted a patent, but despite the many testimonials of farmers about the machine's performance, and much publicity, he couldn't interest anyone in a sale. The hilly country of Virginia was not suited to effective use of the reaper. McCormick retreated from the still-born reaper business, and joined his father in the making of pig iron. By 1839, following the Panic of 1837, the iron business was in collapse. Half the McCormick land went to creditors; the rest was heavily mortgaged. Nothing remained but the reaper patent, and creditors thought it worthless.

Slowly McCormick's fortune changed. He tried again to sell the reaper, and managed to make two sales in 1840, then six in 1842, 39 in 1843 and in 1844, 50 machines, at $100 each. These machines were all made at Walnut Creek. In 1844 McCormick took his first trip west, and saw the vast flatland ready for cultivation. The potential for the reaper business, he knew, was as limitless as the wheatland extending far to the horizon. McCormick moved his business to Chicago in 1847, and by the end of the 1850 harvest, over 4,500 McCormick reapers had been sold throughout the country. McCormick continued to patent improvements until 1858, and then began to buy patents to manufacture and sell. His greatest honor came in 1851 at the London Exposition. The reaper was awarded a grand prize and *The London Times* declared that it was an invention comparable in importance to the Spinning Jenny and the power loom.

Among other American exhibits which gained some attention and prizes was that of the Prouty and Mears draft plow which was cheap, light, strong, with an adaptable coulter. Other farming tools such as hoes, pitch forks, axes and shovels were also judged superior to those widely used in Europe.

With the realization that fruits and vegetables were fresher tasting the sooner canned or preserved after picking, there was a rush of inventive devices such as corn huskers, corn knifes, pea shellers, improved cherrystoners, apple peelers and corers, and vegetable and pickle sorters. John Heinz, the brother of Henry J. Heinz, who founded the 57 varieties industry, patented a pickle sorter in 1879. As the company specialized in sauces, mustards, pickles, jellies, preserves, fruit butters, any labor-saving device was most welcome. The pickle sorter, their ads boasted, separated cucumbers with a greater degree of uniformity of size and accuracy of count than possible by hand sorting. John, known for his "mechanical bent," left the company in 1888 to go West.

Although tomatoes were successfully processed commercially by the chief gardener of Lafayette College in the 1840's, the public could not overcome its centuries' old belief that these "love apples" were poisonous. They gingerly began to accept tomato products in the 1870's, with ketchup one of Heinz's first successful products in 1876. By the 1880's a conveyor belt processing method had been perfected to can vegetables at the Norton Brothers Company Plant, in Indiana. By the 1890's, food processing had become one of the largest industries, supplying fruits, meats and vegetables for a large domestic market and for foreign armies.

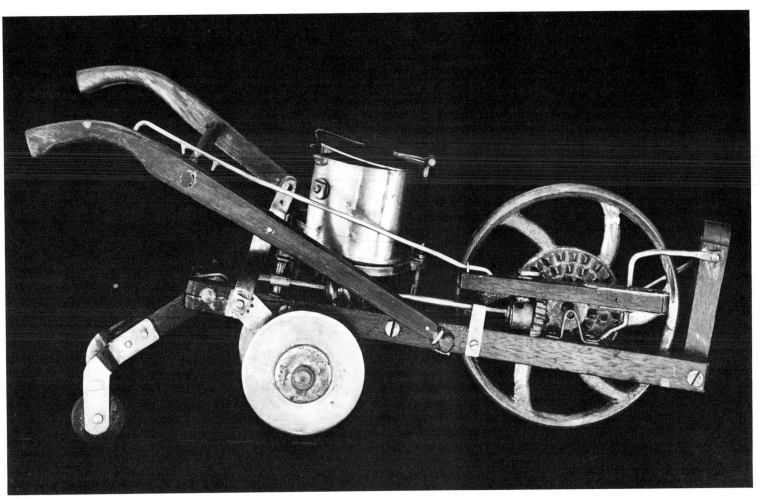

Improved Corn Planter, George W. Hendricks, Rushville, Ind., Aug. 6, 1872. With the machine in motion, the front plow forms a furrow and seeds fall into it from a conductor with holes on the bottom and a loose ball on top. The amount of seed can be regulated by levers. Last, the rear bar and wheel brings soil back over the planted seed. Patent No. 130,220.

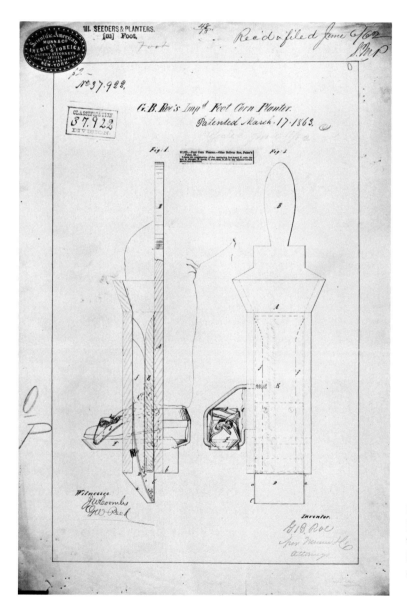

Improved Foot Corn Planter, G. B. Roe, Paine's Point, Ill., Mar. 17, 1863. A device the farmer would attach to his shoe, with a lever which would project the seed into a hole made by the pointed end of the planter. Application drawing. Patent No. 37,922.

FOOT CORN PLANTER.

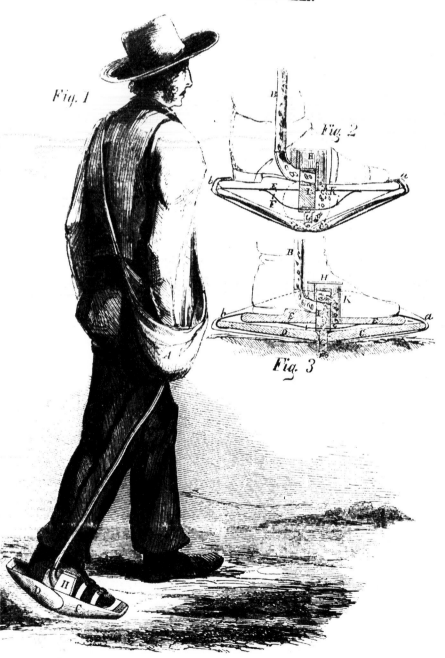

Fig. 1

Fig. 2

Fig. 3

Catalog drawing of a foot corn planter. An attachment to the seed sack carries the hand-apportioned grains directly into the furrow. It was better than stooping down to plant each hill, and less wasteful than scattering the seed. Still it was a slow process and it, in turn, stimulated the improvements of the single and double row drills which enabled the farmer to plant an average of twelve to fifteen acres a day.

Grindstone Frame, J. E. Hoppen, Newark, N.J., Jan. 7, 1879.
An adjustable trough which may be raised or lowered to fit
the diameter of any stone, and easily detached for cleaning.
To this, the inventor also added a movable pedal, arranged
on a swivel, that could be used on either side of the frame by
the operator's right or left foot. Patent No. 211,096.

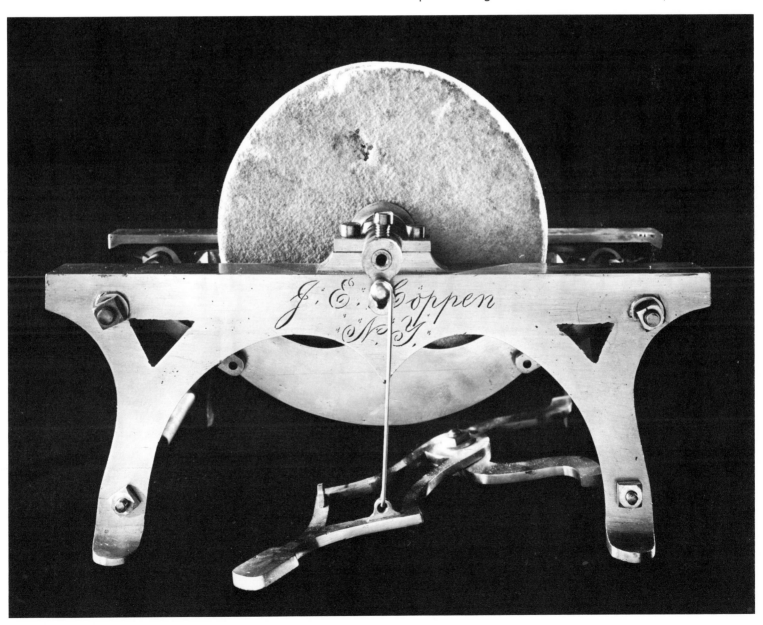

Improved Plow, James Oliver, South Bend, Ind., Apr. 18, 1877. Oliver's most successful invention was of great practicality when plowing furrows of different width, changing from two horses to three, or changing the balance of the plow. All of this can be done by loosening the bolts, shifting the beam and tightening the bolts back up again. The machine consists of an arm or bracket secured to the standard and beam, and is constructed in such a way as to permit lateral movement of the beam relative to the bracket. Patent No. 190,510.

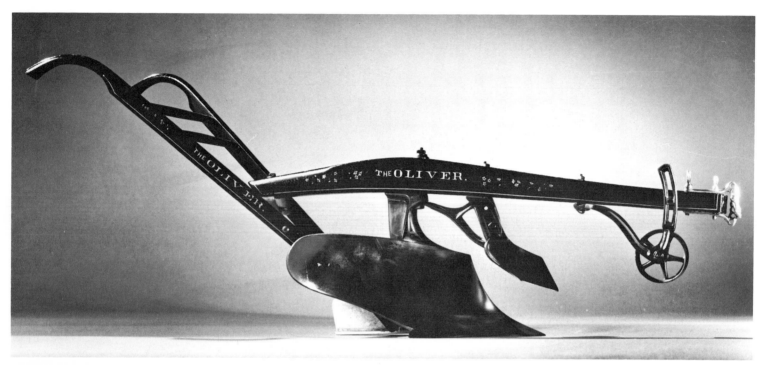

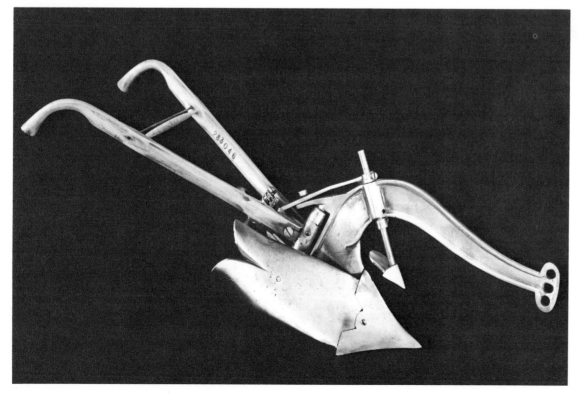

Side-Hill Plow, William Strait, Oneonta, N. Y., October 5, 1880. The invention consists of a reversible single mold-board jointer with double-edged point and land-sides. The mold-board is adapted to operate on the right or left. The handles shift, and thus reverse the jointer, so that the operator can walk in the furrow. Patent No. 233,046.

Advertisement of the McCormick Reaper, 1845. The ad included improvements made since the issuance of the original patent in 1834. It was not until the 1840's that McCormick began to sell his machine in any sizeable numbers. A successful exhibit at the 1851 London Exhibition brought him world fame and capital investment.

M'Cormick's REAPER.

PATENTED 1845.

M'CORMICK'S REAPER.

Right, McCormick Reaper parts as delivered in four crates with directions. All of his reapers came with a written, money-back guarantee; prices were published and fixed; sales were made on terms with credit; field tests and competitions were promoted and publicized.

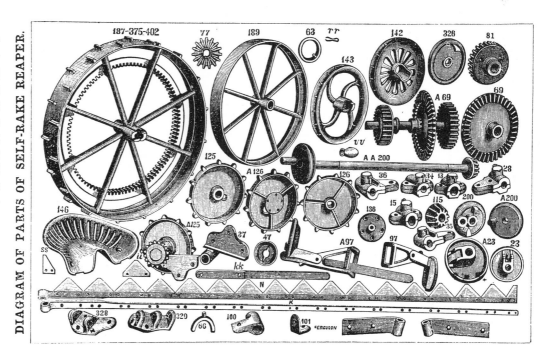

DIAGRAM OF PARTS OF SELF-RAKE REAPER.

Wagon-Platform Gearing, Archibald S. Wakely, Milford, Mich., Feb. 19, 1880. Wakely intended to make the platform more durable by the use of metal rods running through its length. "By the rods passing through the end piece, . . . I am enabled to take up any rattle or looseness of the parts caused by wear, by simply turning the nuts upon the outer ends of the truss-rods." Patent No. 233,648.

Improved Sifting Device, Joseph Hobbs, Mediapolis, Iowa, Apr. 18, 1879. The machine is operated by a rear crank and designed for thorough and efficient sifting. It was to be used for grain or sand. Hobbs held several other patents including those for improved gates, a combined square and bevel, and a weather board gauge or thermometer. Patent No. 214,040.

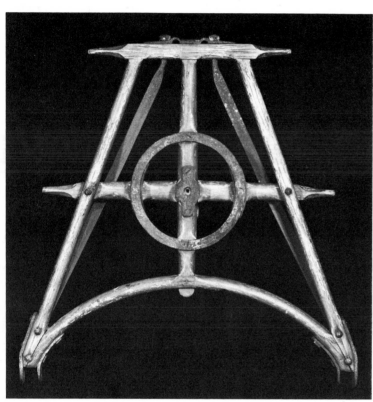

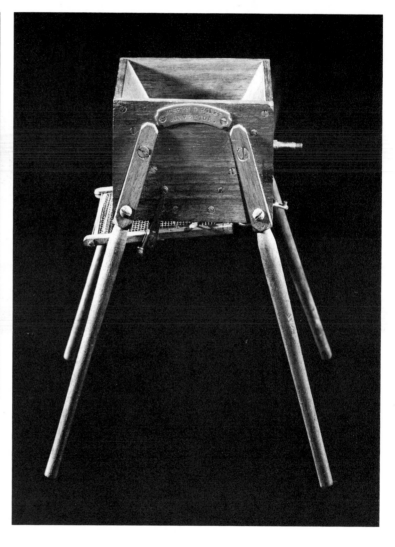

Potato Digger, Amos N. Smiley, Bangor, Maine, Feb. 23, 1878, Patent No. 205,310. The rotary diggers of this Down East contraption are arranged spirally on a shaft; the fingers send the potatoes toward the center, sift out the soil, and facilitate the subsequent gathering. The depth of the diggers is controlled by levers.

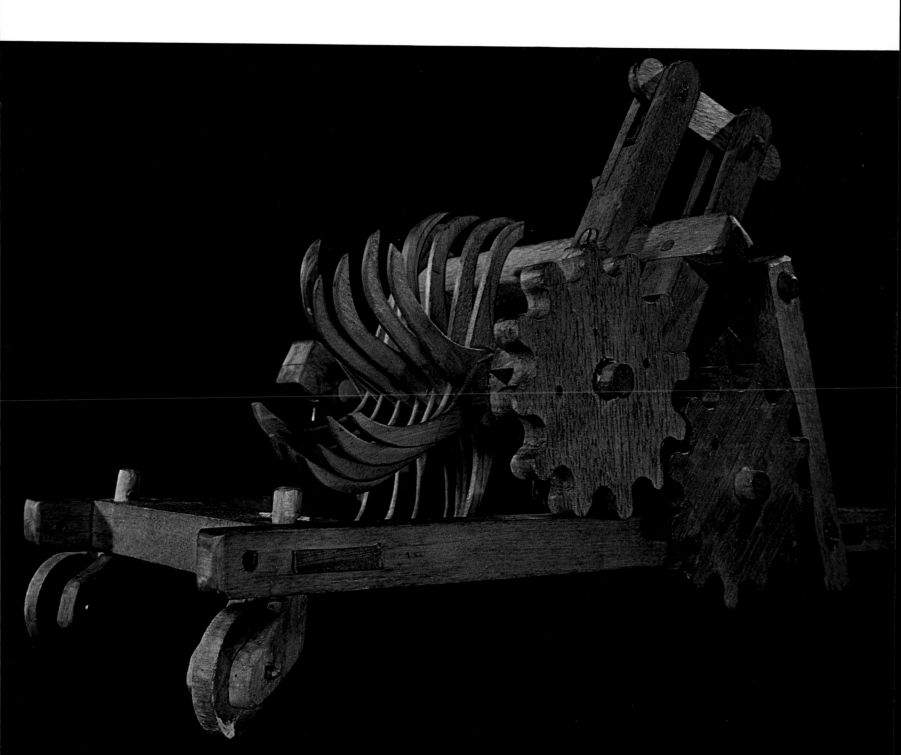

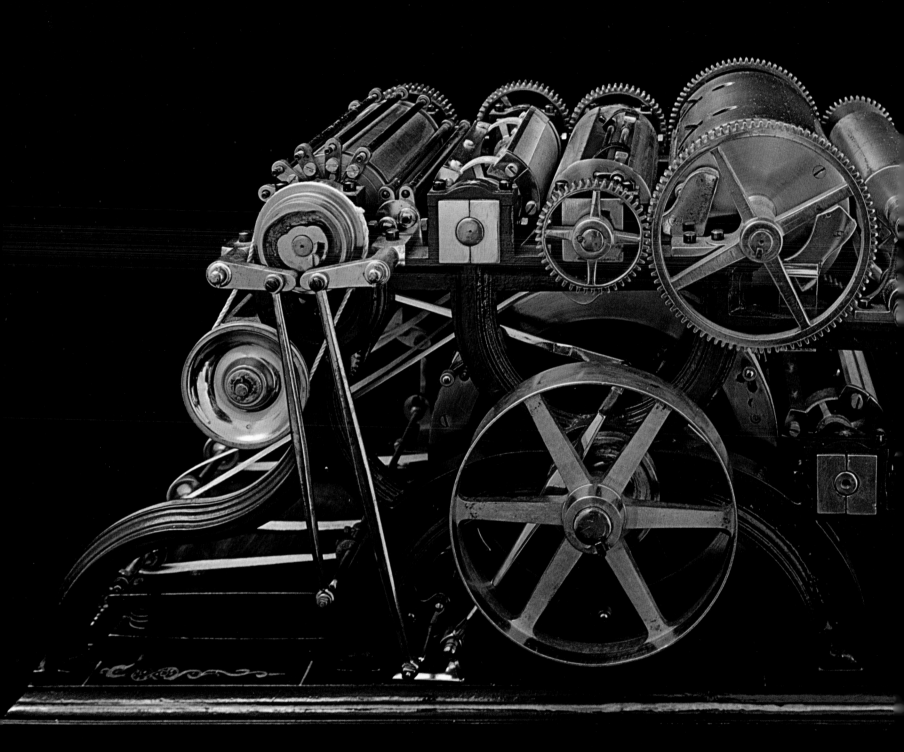

At left, **Printing Press,** William Bullock, Pittsburgh, Penn., April 14, 1863, Patent No. 38,200. The inventor devised a simple delivery apparatus which continually feeds a fast operating press, one that can print on both sides of the sheet simultaneously and run safely at a speed of 6,000 revolutions per hour.
Below, **Printing Press,** Stephen P. Ruggles, Boston, Mass., May 10, 1859, Patent No. 23,951. A coarse and a fine screw works alternately on this hand press to control the depth of the impression.

Wind Engine, John Cook, Kirkwood, Ill., May 29, 1878, Patent No. 209,862. The inventor stated this machine could be attached to mills, pumps, thrashing machines, plows, mowers, road wagons, navigating vessels – any stationary mechanism requiring momentum. When the wind moves the sails, a center shaft is rotated and this, through the gearing, communicates motion to the axle and on to the wheels.

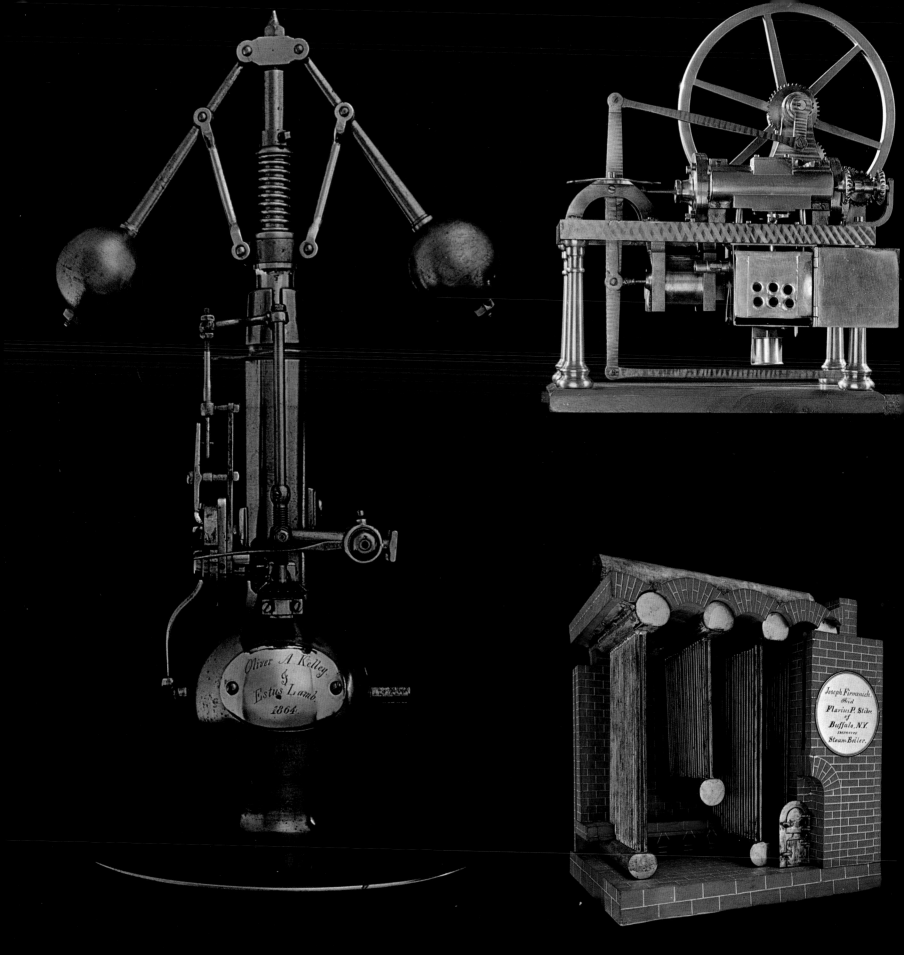

Oliver A. Kelley
&
Estus Lamb
1864.

Joseph Firmenich,
and
Flavius P. Stiles
of
Buffalo, N.Y.
IMPROVED
Steam Boiler.

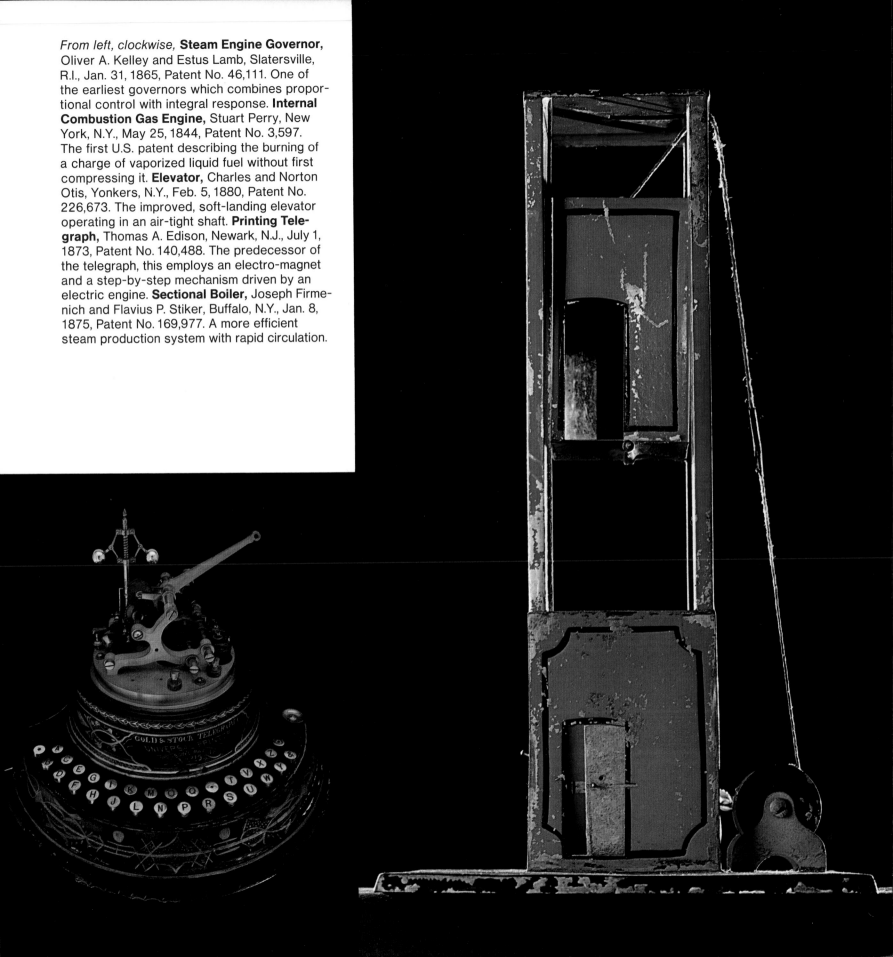

From left, clockwise, **Steam Engine Governor,** Oliver A. Kelley and Estus Lamb, Slatersville, R.I., Jan. 31, 1865, Patent No. 46,111. One of the earliest governors which combines proportional control with integral response. **Internal Combustion Gas Engine,** Stuart Perry, New York, N.Y., May 25, 1844, Patent No. 3,597. The first U.S. patent describing the burning of a charge of vaporized liquid fuel without first compressing it. **Elevator,** Charles and Norton Otis, Yonkers, N.Y., Feb. 5, 1880, Patent No. 226,673. The improved, soft-landing elevator operating in an air-tight shaft. **Printing Telegraph,** Thomas A. Edison, Newark, N.J., July 1, 1873, Patent No. 140,488. The predecessor of the telegraph, this employs an electro-magnet and a step-by-step mechanism driven by an electric engine. **Sectional Boiler,** Joseph Firmenich and Flavius P. Stiker, Buffalo, N.Y., Jan. 8, 1875, Patent No. 169,977. A more efficient steam production system with rapid circulation.

Improved Reaper, William N. Whiteley, Springfield, Ohio, Apr. 25, 1877. One of hundreds of improvements on reapers, mowers, threshers and combines of the mid to late-nineteenth century. This, as with many others, was successfully manufactured. By 1860 there were over 80,000 reapers in operation, and the West's wheat harvest was beginning to assume great importance. Patent No. 197,192.

New and Useful Improvement in Bale-Tie Fastenings, Curran Battle, Warrenton, Ga., May 7, 1878. The buckle for the bale band is adapted to slide or be adjusted at one end, and to bite and clamp at any point. Simple to construct, it was also easy to adjust to different sized bales. Patent No. 203,401.

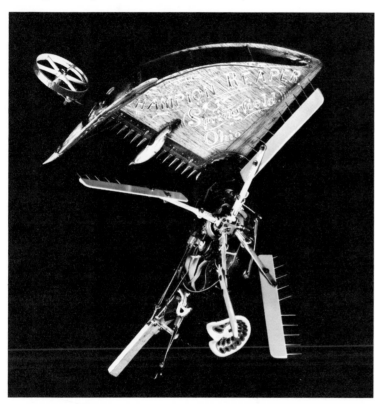

Alonzo Johnson
Ass'r To.
S. Bissell & A.B. West

Calculating Machine

IX. From Workshop to Assembly Line

When Alexander Hamilton compiled his *Report on Manufacturing* in 1791, he concluded that the prosperity of America would depend on a great increase in machines and a labor force to operate them. In turn, domestic demand for goods would grow, and, eventually, foreign markets would be established. He was confident that the labor problem could be solved through emigration and development of that "peculiar aptitude for mechanical improvement." In brief, his argument is as perfect a classical statement of capitalism, American style, as has ever been penned. The fulfillment of the Hamiltonian vision meant the end of the individual craftsman and the rise of the industrial mass.

By the mid-nineteenth century, the industrial revolution had worked its wonders. In New England the process had begun earlier with the cotton mills. Lucy Larcom, in her autobiography, *A New England Girlhood*, recalled that she started working at the Lowell, Massachusetts, mill at age eleven, changing bobbins for as many as thirteen hours a day and for a wage of no more than $1 per week. Gone were the days, she wrote, of pleasure watching "Aunt Hannah spinning on her flax wheel, keeping time . . . to some quaint old tune with her foot upon the treadle." The rules forbade all books and the plant overseer had a deskful of confiscated Bibles! But it wasn't all bad, Lucy concluded, "On the whole, it was far from being a disagreeable place to stay in. The girls were bright-looking and neat, and everything was kept clean and shining. The effect of the whole was rather attractive to strangers."

In later years, visitors to such factories found them much less appealing to the eye. The surroundings had become shabby and crowded; wages had not kept pace with pro-

duction. And, perhaps most important, the original excitement and wonder which met the introduction of new machinery, new methods of doing things, had long since died away. But the American inventor was still at work, cultivating, in the words of Tocqueville, "the arts that serve to render life easy in preference to those whose object is to adorn it." In time, through the inventor's skill, life would indeed be made easier for the mass of people that Hamilton envisioned manning the machines of industry, but no more beautiful.

Elisha Graves Otis was a mechanic for a Yonkers bedstead company in 1852. The company wanted a hoist built for hauling merchandise to the second floor. He devised the necessary device and ingeniously added wagon springs underneath the platform which would catch on grooves of the track if the rope should break. Totally unimpressed with his own invention, Otis was preparing to join the California gold rush when he received orders for two "safety hoisters." In 1853 he opened his own workshop for building them, and found himself at the end of the year with sales totaling $900, and an inventory of $122.71, a second-hand lathe, two oil cans and his account book.

Otis decided to take a dramatic step and to demonstrate his safety device at the 1853 New York Crystal Palace Exhibition. In front of many curious spectators, he rode up to the ceiling in one of his hoists, and then ordered the rope cut. The safety device worked and his industry was established. Before 1857 all the elevators made were for freight, and then a New York department store installed one for passengers. The Astor Hotel installed its first Otis elevator in 1858, run by hand. When Elisha Otis died in 1861, his sons Charles and Norton took over the company. Both as mechanically gifted as their father, they patented many improvements on the elevator as they progressed from steam to hydraulic to electric-operated machinery. The Otis brothers gained international fame when they supplied the elevators rising 380 feet to the second platform of the Eiffel Tower at Paris' 1889 Universal Exposition. The technological and economic effect of the invention and improvement of the elevator—as if to confirm Hamilton's argument about mechanization— on modern society is beyond any means of calculation.

Opposite page, Calculating Apparatus, Alonzo Johnson, Springfield, Mass., Dec. 22, 1868. A machine designed to indicate the sum, or amount of numbers to be added together, within certain defined limits. It also indicates the numbers which have already been added. Patent No. 85,229.

The manufacturing of printing presses was a thriving industry in the early 1800's when America was publishing more than 150 newspapers. Although the early presses were modeled after the English, improvements were quick in coming. The hand press was markedly improved by George Clymer in 1813. A steam-powered, revolving cylinder press, invented by Robert Hoe and his son, Richard, in 1847, revolutionized the printing industry. Newspapers, building their circulation by being the "first on the street" with the news, needed much faster presses. With the Hoe press, the "Lightning," using four impression cylinders, 8,000 papers per hour could be printed. The press had a type cylinder fifteen feet in diameter, with type arranged on column-wide flat surfaces, and capable of printing up to ten impressions. All of the major city newspapers were equipped with the Hoe Lightning 1860. Robert Hoe had built the first simple cylinder press in 1828.

William Bullock, a mechanic/inventor, supplied some of the features lacking in the Hoe in 1863 with his web-perfecting press. It fed the paper from a continuous roll and printed both sides in one operation. With added improvements, it could automatically perform every function save folding.

In 1820 when Englishman Charles Babbage complained while correcting many errors in a mathematical table: "I wish to God these calculations had been executed by steam," his colleague replied, "It is entirely possible." Babbage worked for many years trying to perfect his "analytic engine," but never succeeded because many of the necessary skills and material were not to be developed until the twentieth century. There were, however, substitutes. The first key driven American machine was patented in 1850, and thousands of calculating machines were patented during the second half of the century, most of them of compact design. Nearly all used the mechanism devised by Blaise Pascal in the seventeenth century for addition, and the "stepped drum" mechanism based on Pascal's geared wheel developed in the following century for multiplication by G. W. von Leibniz. F. S. Baldwin improved this mechanism, and in 1887 D. E. Felt patented the first comptometer, and in the following year W. S. Burroughs patented a key set adding machine with a crank. Keeping up with the numbers in an industrialized society was to become a very big business, especially with the introduction of the typewriter in 1867 by C. Latham Sholes.

The 1876 Philadelphia International Centennial Exhibition showed the products of the century-old nation to good advantage, but it was at the 1878 Paris Universal Exposition that the American industrial genius was most evident. Ten grand prizes were awarded to distinguished Americans, among them Thomas Edison for his light bulb and phonograph, McCormick for his binder/reaper. By this time, many American manufacturers had established offices in Europe; Singer was one of the first. The market abroad for the mechanical genius of the New World was firmly established, and America had become synomomous with technological progress.

Left, Hand Printing Press, James Phelps, New York, N.Y., Nov. 2, 1858. The inventor called this the "Phelps Economist Printing Press." He combined the ink rollers with a shield and the rising and falling platen so that material could be printed precisely within the desired margins. Patent No. 21,980.

Right, Hand Printing Press, Alonzo Newbury and Bolivar Newbury, Windham Center, N.Y., July 5, 1859. This perfectly made brass model exhibits an improvement in hand printing. It includes a table which will rotate to evenly distribute the ink in the rollers. Patent No. 24,655.

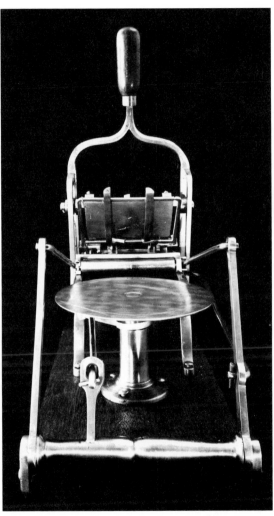

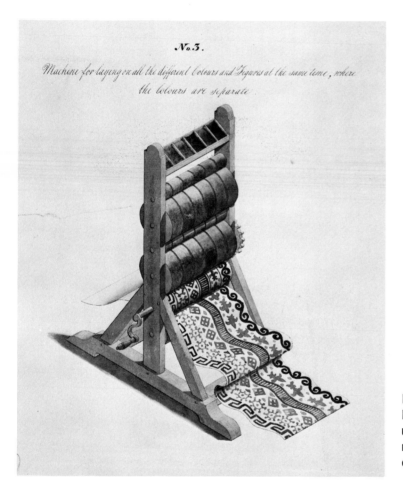

No. 3.

Machine for laying on all the different Colours and Figures at the same time, where the colours are separate.

Improvement in Multicolor Rotary Printing for Wall Paper and Fabrics, Peter Force, Washington, D.C., Aug. 22, 1822. By using many rollers, each with different colors or designs, the material could be colored and printed at the same time. Watercolor application drawing by the Patent Office.

Alarm Bell, Benjamin Freymuth, Philadelphia, Penn., Dec. 22, 1821. Operated by means of a timing device, the alarm could be adjusted to serve train stations, school houses, or in the home. Watercolor application drawing by the Patent Office.

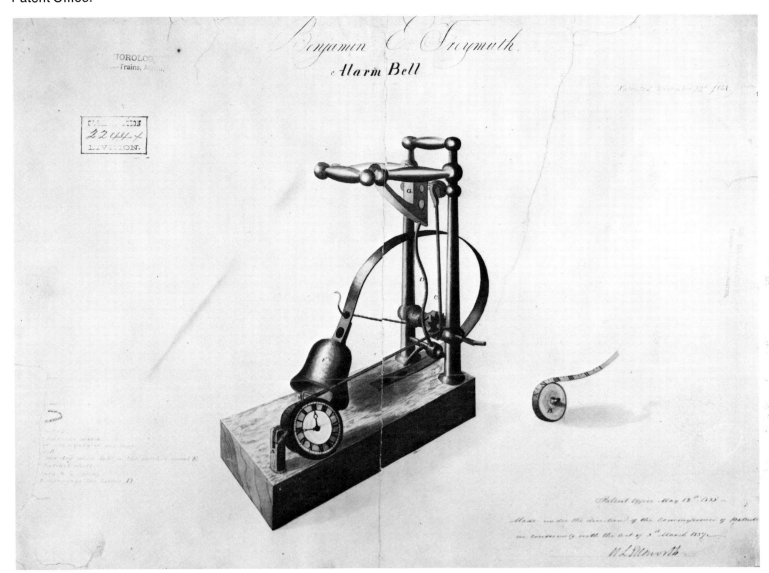

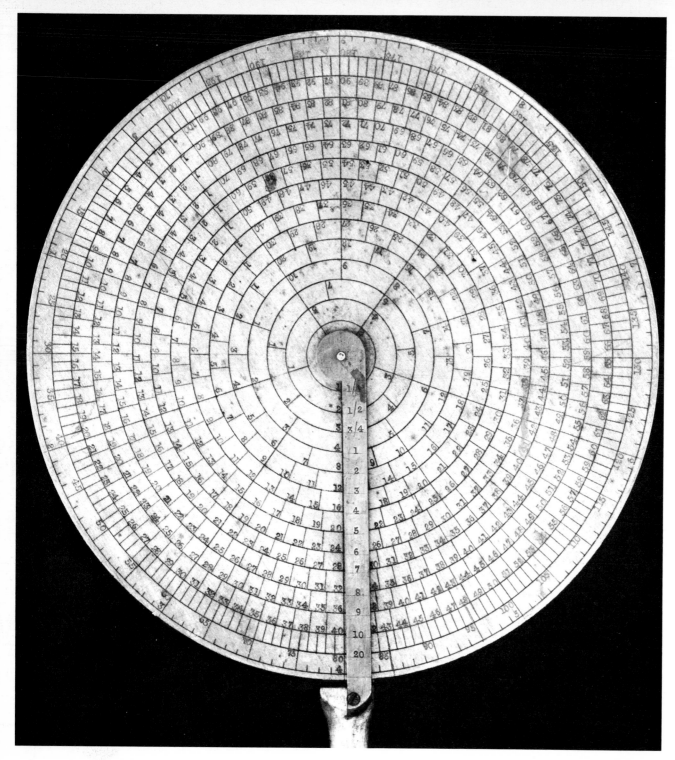

Calculating Device, James D. Smith, Brantingham, N.Y., Nov. 24, 1857. A multiplying device with a handle for greater facility. It employs a rotary disk, graduated on one side and numbered to form a table, which would be used with a stationary graduated index. Patent No. 18,711.

Opposite page, Improved Adding Machine, Gustavus Linderoos, Point Arena, Calif., June 24, 1873. This machine would tally a number of small numbers while retaining the whole. Each revolving disk represents a volume of different numbers: the large disk, 1-100, the right-hand disk, 100-1000, etc. Patent No. 140,146.

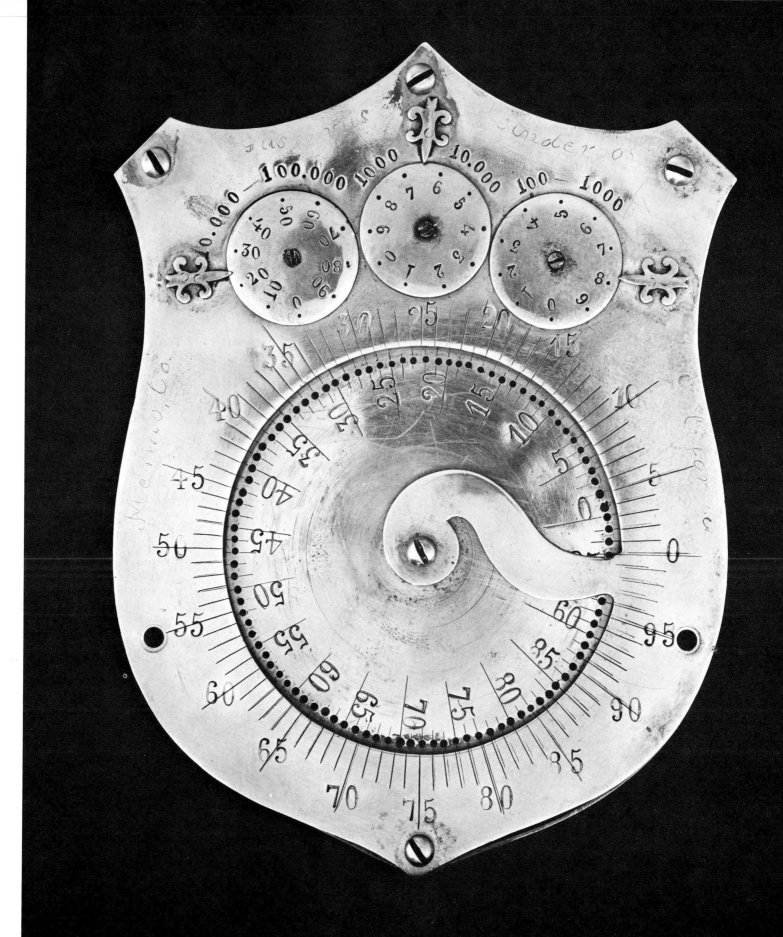

Improved Adding Machine, David Carroll, Spring Creek, Penn., May 2, 1876. The machine includes keys for each of the nine digits, arranged for two to be worked by each finger of the left hand and the thumb. Each key turns the unit wheel the number of times as indicated. Patent No. 176,833.

Calculating Machine, Dr. Joseph B. Alexander, Baltimore, Md., Mar. 15, 1864. With a combination of separate levers and sets of wheels for greater calculating speed, the machine uses sets of figured drums which add, subtract, multiply, and divide. Patent No. 41,898.

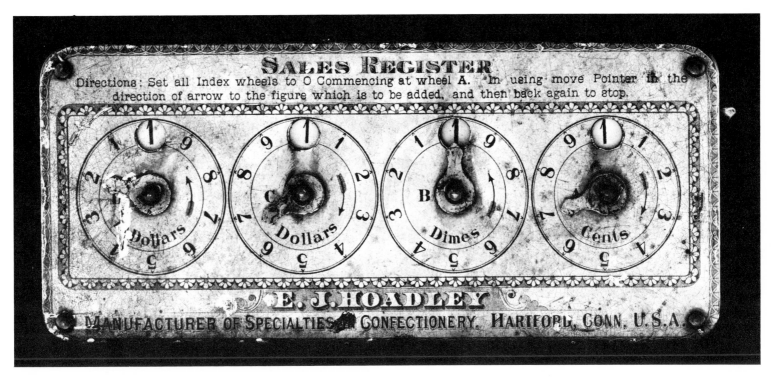

Improved Adding Machine, William Lang, Brooklyn, N.Y., July 1, 1890. A cheap and convenient adding device for store keepers and others who have to quickly add small sums while filling orders for customers. It is made of stamped sheet metal, and can be manufactured, assembled, and sold at low cost. The rotary disks turn independently of each other. The underside of disks are punched with ratchet teeth which engage with ratchet wheels. Patent No. 431,365.

Machine for Scouring, Blacking, and Finishing Leather, F. William Rust, Umatilla, Ore., Nov. 10, 1868. The scouring apparatus is suspended with a weight and lever, and can be adjusted to the thickness of the leather. Rubbing blocks are provided with brushes to clean, spread the blacking, and for scouring stone or glass. The hollow pendulum contains blacking. Patent No. 84,001.

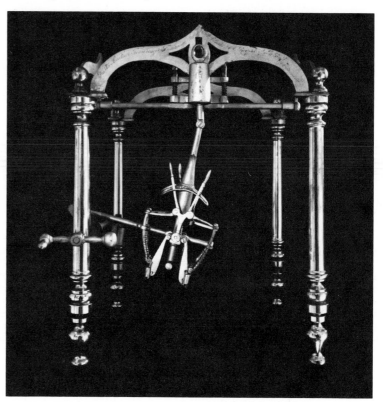

Jet Condenser for Steam Engines, John Houpt, Springtown, Penn., Mar. 18, 1873. An improvement designed to facilitate simpler, cheaper, effective and accurate devices for operating valves of jet condensers. It is a simplification of an earlier patent of Houpt's. Patent No. 136,918.

Opposite page, Improvement in Solar Camera, Lyman G. Bigelow, Albion, Mich., Nov. 5, 1867. An enlarger which is set on a tripod attached to gears which governed the position of the condensing lens so that it coincides with the maximum degree of sunlight. Clockwork is also attached, and moves the lens to correspond to the earth's motion, thus insuring a uniform intensity of light during the time used. Patent No. 70,509.

Portable Forge, Charles Hammelmann, Buffalo, N.Y., June 24, 1879. All the mechanical parts are attached to the hearth, and not the legs, thereby rendering the forge more compact and portable. Everything is protected by the roof when used outdoors. The curvature of the wings catches the air, thus giving a superior blast and helping to expel the air. Patent No. 252,103.

Apparatus for Measuring, Controlling, and Registering Liquids, Francois Jean Joseph Delori, Snaeskerke, Belgium, Feb. 12, 1878. The inventor, a sugar manufacturer, created this device for regulating and registering the volume and density of alcohol, beet root juices, beer, and other liquids. It was to be used by distillers, sugar manufacturers, brewers, and government agencies for determining excise duty. An alarm indicates when the apparatus was full. The filling process is equipped with a timer, to protect the manufacturer from "malicious" or thirsty workmen. Gauges indicate the amount inside. Patent No. 200,184.

Magneto-Electric Machine, Thomas Edison, Menlo Park, N.J., Sept. 10, 1879. One of many Edison improvements which led him to the development of a self-exciting dynamo. This invention was never manufactured, but served the inventor's exploratory purpose. Patent No. 222,881.

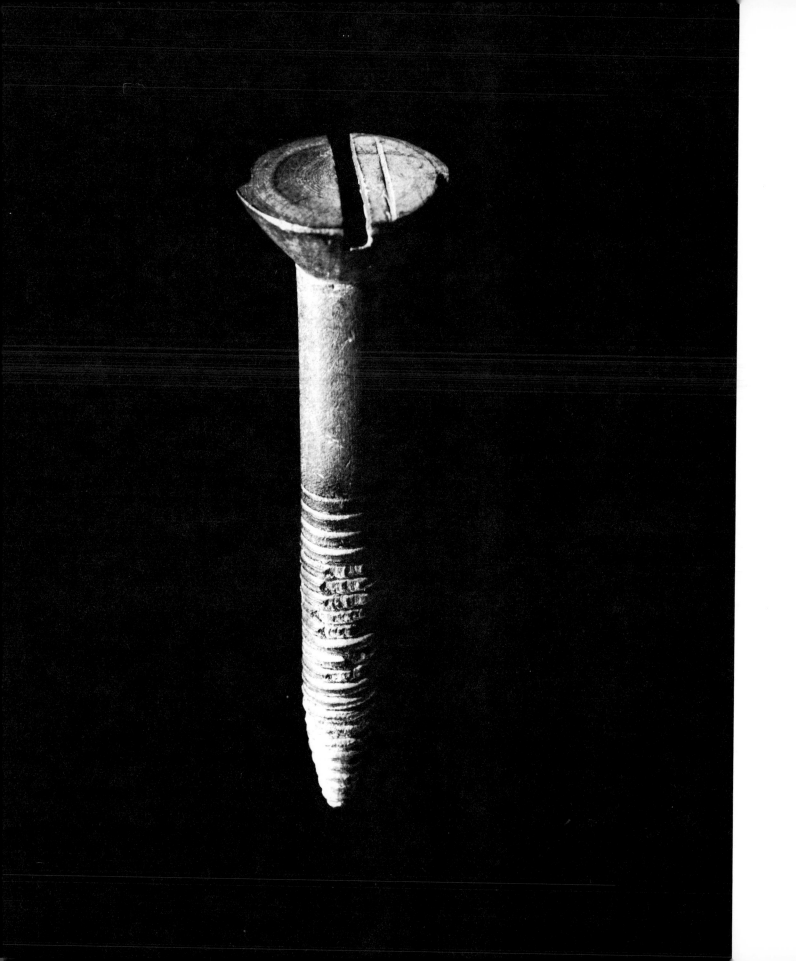

X. Tools to Make Things Work

Tools and the men who knew how to use them were the most valuable resources for survival in the wilderness. Most of the early settlers were practical and, like the founders of the Plymouth Colony, came equipped with tools for their respective crafts—blacksmithing, tailoring, cooperage, printing, stonemasonry, carpentry. Throughout the Colonial period, the design of English and Dutch tools was adapted to the new and peculiar problems encountered in America. The English axe, for instance, was too heavy and clumsy for the clearing of heavy woods. What emerged under new conditions was a thinner, wider, sharper blade attached to a handle shaped especially for its owner. In the right hands, the broadaxe would hew timber as smoothly as a saw.

It was not until the mid-nineteenth century, however, that Americans gained a reputation as fine toolmakers. It was in the development of machines for the making of nails and screws, and in Connecticut's clockmaking industry, that the need for drastically new tools became evident. Mass production along assembly lines required fine tooling and artisans capable of operating them.

An improved turret lathe, invented by Stephen Fitch in 1845, produced good machine tools in great quantity. The Sharp machine for making screws won a prize at the Paris 1867 Exposition. The American plane and circular saw were recognized there as being far superior to those from any other country. Eli Whitney was the first to apply interchangeable parts manufacturing in his musket factory in 1800. He was followed by Thomas Blanchard, a Massachusetts machinist, who invented a gunstock machine which turned out stocks according to pattern, and a turning lathe which he used for the treatment of leather. Whitney and Blanchard were followed by Samuel Colt, Chauncey Jerome and countless others in what became known as the "American System" of manufacture. It was this same process which was used for the production of sewing and agricultural machines. Whitney successfully demonstrated his system to the visiting Secretary of War at his plant at Whitneyville, Connecticut, by assembling ten muskets from parts randomly selected from different stacks. In the 1840's, Cyrus McCormick was able to ship his reaper to a farmer in four crates with instructions for assembling. Specially designed tools and dies were the indispensable ingredients in creating the successful mixture of parts—whether for a reaper, clock, sewing machine or musket.

The Civil War increased the need for improved arms and their manufacture. One mechanic, Christopher Miner Spencer, invented a lever action repeating rifle which the Confederates, still using single-shot firearms, described as a gun the Yankee could "load in the morning and shoot all day." When the war ended, Spencer turned his mind to peaceful invention. He developed a machine which made sewing machine spools, one that automatically produced screws, and the automatic turret lathe. The turret lathe was developed in the nineteenth century by a number of New England toolmakers. Spencer's innovation was the introduction of adjustable cams which could be used to engage the workpiece of the lathe to any cycle of work. It is perhaps the most important development in tool manufacture, used for every kind of tool from precision instrument to those employed to produce the engine blocks of a Ford motor.

Accuracy, of course, is the key to the success of the interchangeable parts system. One had to check the "jig" for any wearing that might slightly alter the size of a particular object. During the Civil War production of firearms, the various armories developed gauges for each part of the manufacturing process, and even for each operation. They were awkward and expensive, and soon a different type replaced them, the so-called "Go-No-Go" gauges. Two sets of measurements were taken by means of these, the largest and smallest acceptable dimension of the part to be checked. Unless the part fitted into the "Go" gauge, it was unacceptable. The gauges were readily adopted in all parts of the country as they were cheap and easy to use.

Opposite page, Wood Screw, G. Freeman, New York, N.Y., Sept. 11, 1860. One of twenty-seven patents issued for wood screws between 1790 and 1873. Freeman's is designed with a grooved gimlet, to facilitate the penetration of wood. This is to eliminate the usual wood-splitting and damage done to the screw, especially when working with hard or close-grained wood. Patent No. 29,963.

The ultimate instrument with which to take accurate measurements and the first practical device for widespread use was the Vernier caliper, invented by Joseph R. Brown in 1851. It was based on the scale proposed by Joseph Vernier in the seventeenth century which slides along a larger graduated instrument and indicates fractional parts of divisions. Its accuracy was to 0.001 of an inch. In 1869 Lucian Sharpe marketed a micrometer for measuring sheet metal to 0.004 of an inch. By the 1880's, all machine shops in the United States were using this device. As production and technology became more specialized, even more accurate instruments were invented which could measure to a few millionths of an inch.

The development of toolmaking in the United States has closely paralleled that of manufacturing methods. Americans still look to other countries for some of the best of both simple and complex instruments, but the history of invention in this field has been astonishing. With the coming of the age of electronics, the demand for highly intricate "tools" to make sophisticated machinery work is being met each day of the week, as the overworked employees of the Patent Office can testify.

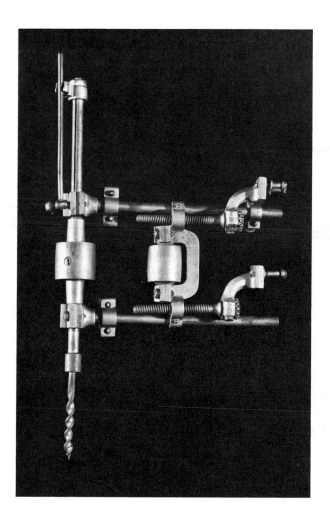

Right, Improved Drill Press, inventor unknown. His improvement will forever remain a secret, among many from the O. Rundle Gilbert Collection.

Convertible Carpenter's Square and Bevel, Emile Simonin, Peoria, Ill., Jan. 5, 1876. This ingenious device is so simple in concept that its claim required only one-half a page. "The advantages of this instrument are its convertibility into a square or bevel or angulator with facility, its compactness, and simplicity of construction." The accompanying drawing shows the instrument as a square for trying the angles of solids, as a common square for getting perpendicular lines, and as an angulator, or for striking oblique angles. Patent No. 172,938.

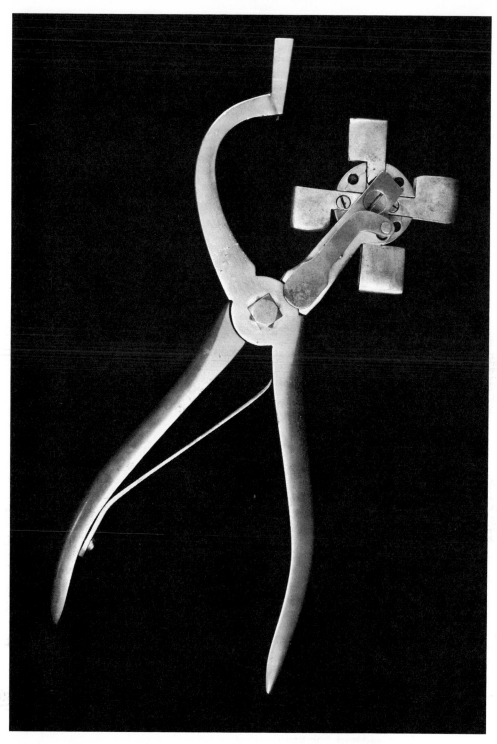

Leather Cutting Punches, Bartlett Bohonon, West Fairless, Vt., Mar. 5, 1879. The hand leather punch is fitted with a revolving head which can hold various sized cutters. These are removable for sharpening and changing of sizes. Patent No. 215,870.

Opposite, Improved Oil-Can, Thomas Fildes, Media, Penn., Apr. 12, 1859. An invention which consists of an ordinary oil can, a long pole (on model this is shortened to a handle) and a clamp to fix the two together. With a hammer device which strikes the oil-can's bottom, distant and hard to get to places could be reached without the aid of a stepladder. Patent No. 23,560.

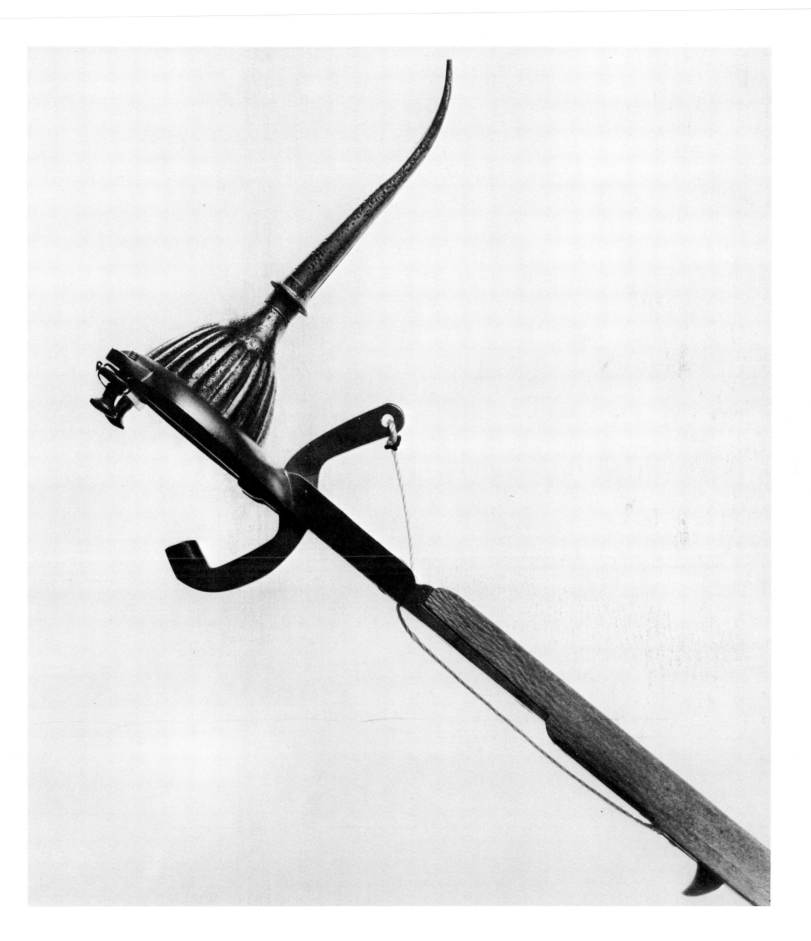

Shears for Cutting Metal, Julius Hornig, Oswego, N.Y., Feb. 7, 1865. An invention which consists of a novel method of using double shears, with the material to be cut held firmly against the cutting edge. Patent No. 46,237.

Right, Improved Heel Cutter, J. H. Bean, Marietta, Ohio, June 22, 1869. This heavy brass model, with a simple branch design, represents the mechanism of a bent lever, a set screw and shaft which would achieve more efficient, faster heel cutting. Patent No. 91,508.

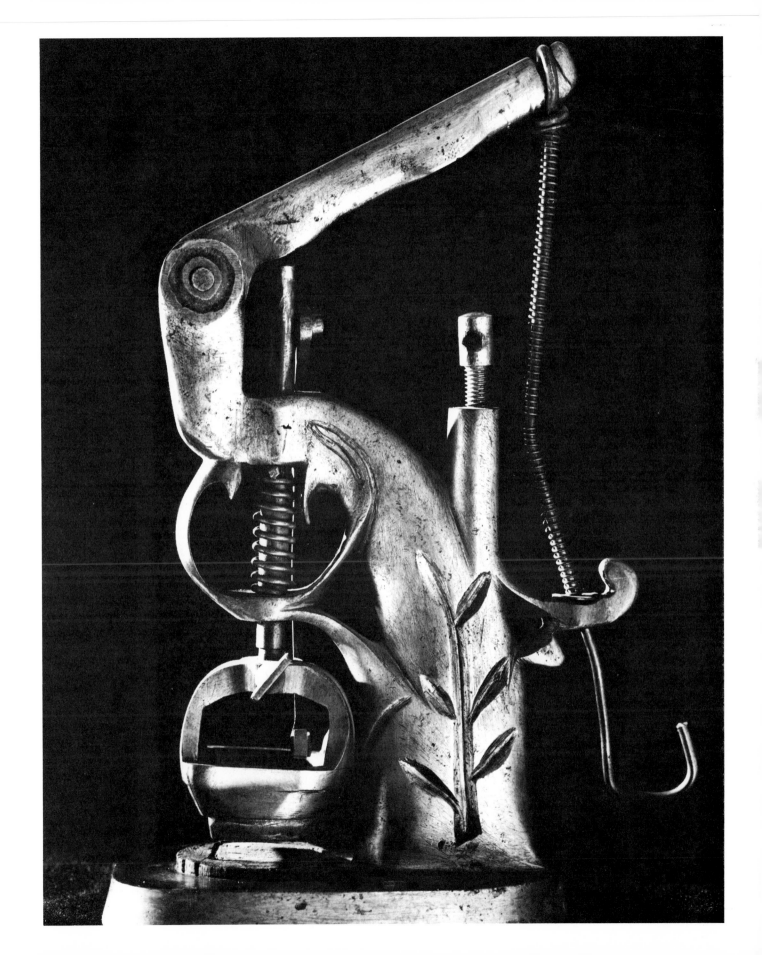

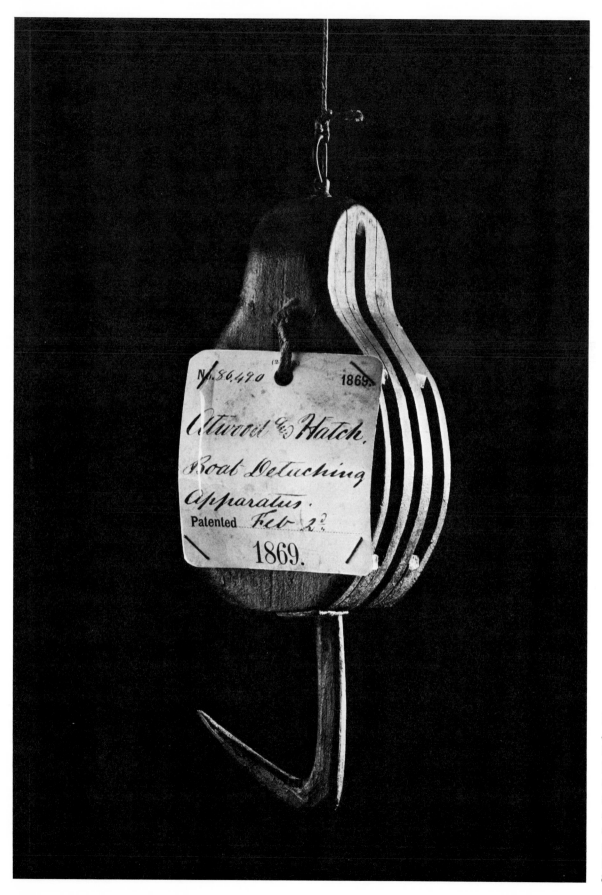

On the tag: *N.86.490 (2) 1869. Attwood & Hatch. Boat Detaching Apparatus. Patented Feb 2d 1869.*

Boat Detaching Apparatus, John Atwood and Thomas M. Hatch, Provincetown, Mass., Feb. 2, 1869. The invention consists of a combined move-able hook and block and spring which could be used to detach a boat. Atwood also patented a process for curing and putting up fish. Patent No. 86,490.

XI. In Defense of the Absurd

"But the fantasies of one day are the deepest realities of a future one."
—Nathaniel Hawthorne

Samuel Sparks Fisher, Commissioner of Patents in 1869 and 1870, when asked what proportion of patented inventions were really useful, replied: "Probably not much more than one-tenth; But let it be remembered, there are few failures so harmless as that of a useless invention. The patent gives it a chance to prove itself worthy of the public patronage. It simply declares that if it be good it shall not be stolen. But if it be useless, nobody would want to steal it."

An invention that no one would want to steal was that of Reuben J. Spalding, the creator of an improved flying machine, illustrated on the jacket of this book. It is not known whether Spalding tested his machine, but if he did, he certainly survived the attempt. Spalding had gone prospecting for gold in Colorado in the 1850's—before turning to the art of invention—and knew how difficult it was to sift the real from the imaginary, but he was not afraid to try.

James Pirsson of New York was another such dauntless individual. He exhibited his double grand pianoforte at the London Crystal Palace Exhibition in 1851. He claimed that four performers could play the instrument at the same time, but Pirsson was never able to find a way to ship the contraption from London. It died still-born.

Reversible Barber Chair, Philip Haberstitch, Dayton, Ohio, Feb. 18, 1873. The seat and back of this barber chair can be reversed by means of an elaborate system of ropes, pulleys, and cogs. In one-and-a-half pages of directions, the inventor never mentions why anyone would want to reverse the back or seat. Perhaps it was a way of automatically dusting off the chair. It could also recline, but fortunately, for the customer, only in one position. Patent No. 135,986.

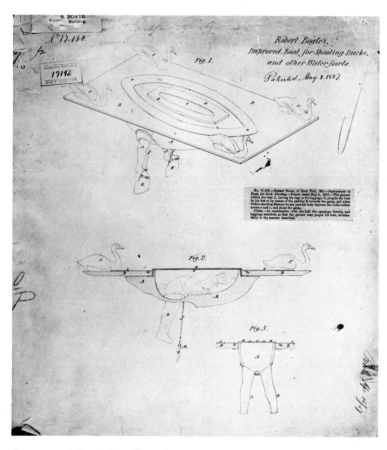

The pretzel, or bretzel (German form), has been around for over 1,500 years. The first reference to it in the New World was penned in 1652 in Albany, New York, when a complaint was filed against one Jochem Wessels, and his wife, Gertrude, for using the best flour in pretzels sold to the Indians. White men were left with only bran. It wasn't until the 1860's that pretzels were produced on a large scale. A German tourist presented a recipe to a Lititz, Penn., baker, who, in turn, passed it on to his apprentice, Julius Sturgis. Sturgis opened and operated the first large pretzel bakery. Machines for assembly line production were fast in coming from the inventors' hands.

Milton Bradley amassed a fortune from the invention of games for the family. An eighth-generation Yankee, he was born in Vienna, Maine, in 1836. He had been brought up to believe that playing cards were the "devil's picture books," and that idle time should always be spent seeking divine grace. His early business career was a checkered one, and, economic depression and unemployment left him with more idle time than he could afford. In 1860, throwing off the Puritan restraints, he started inventing games for himself and others in similar straits. The first of these was "The Checkered Game of Life." The game was first peddled in New York City, and was almost an instant success. By the winter of 1861, he had sold more than 40,000 sets.

During the Civil War, Bradley invented "Games for Soldiers," a light, small kit which contained nine games designed to relieve the tedium of being a foot soldier. They were popular and widely bought up by charities to donate to the troops. Other entertaining pastimes were soon developed such as the rebus puzzle called "Modern Hieroglyphs," "Patriotic Hero, or Who's Traitor?", "Sunday School Cards," "Authors" —many of which are still played today. Eventually, Bradley became interested in the new kindergarten movement, and developed a line of teaching aids and school supplies, including crayons. It was all a concession to nonsense, or so it seemed to many at the time, but Bradley, in retrospect, was a supremely practical inventor. Perhaps he was the greatest —he created a business that was not supposed even to exist in America.

Nathaniel Hawthorne, denying the sentiments of the period, upheld an occasional concession to nonsense. In his allegorical story, *The Hall of Fantasy*, he envisioned a realm of imagination within which one could walk with poets and philosophers of all ages, romantic builders, and also a peculiar kind of dreamer, the inventor. Here one could observe railroad tracks built through air, a tunnel under the sea, a distiller of heat from moonshine, a condenser of morning mist which formed blocks of granite, a lens that produced sunshine out of a lady's smile and tinted her dress with sunset. It all reminded Hawthorne of a trip to the exhibition hall at the Patent Office in Washington, and he concluded, "It may be said, in truth, that there is but half a life—the meaner and earthlier half—for those who never find their way into the hall."

Improved Boat for Shooting Ducks, Robert Bogle, Rock Hill, Md., May 5, 1857. A solution to a duck hunter's dream—a method of swimming among an unsuspected flock and then decimating it. The hunter apparently relied on the quacking of the ducks to determine his proximity as the apparatus seems to lack either a periscope or an underwater viewing glass. Watercolor application drawing. Patent No. 17,192.

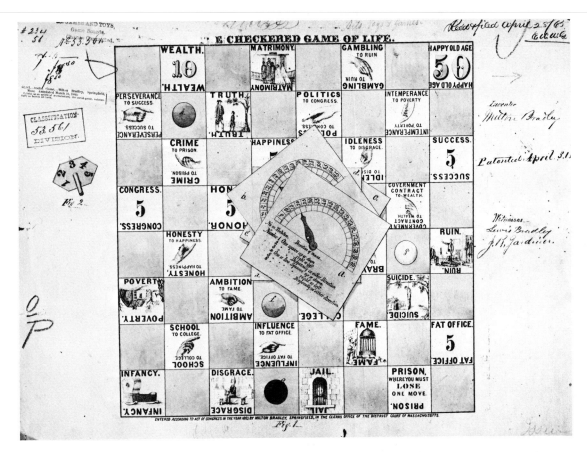

Checkered Game of Life, Milton Bradley, Springfield, Mass., Apr. 3, 1866. The first board game to be developed and marketed in the United States, it is the forerunner of all the popular "social games." Bradley was a Yankee tinkerer who pioneered in kindergarten education, and developed such school room supplies as "flash" cards and crayons. Although modified from the first red and white checkered board, and now simply called "The Game of Life," the game is still one of the favorites sold by this large manufacturer. Watercolor application drawing. Patent No. 53,561.

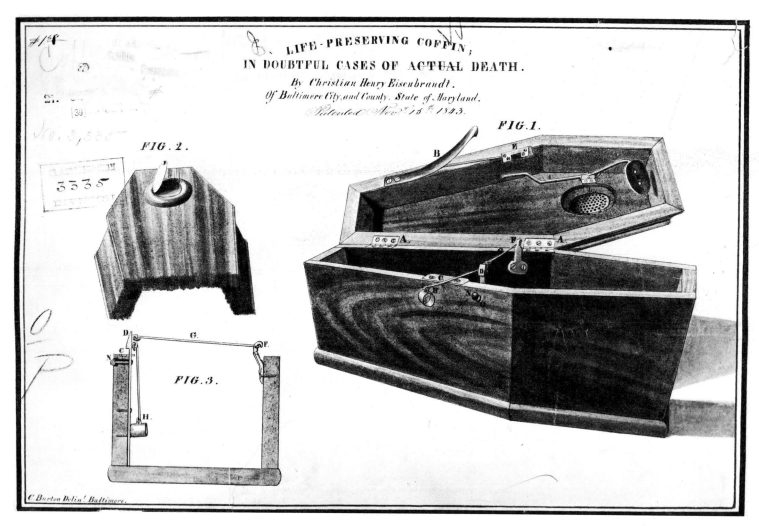

Life Preserving Coffin, In Doubtful Cases of Actual Death, Christian Henry Eisenbrandt, Baltimore, Md., Nov. 15, 1843. This is one of hundreds of such devices presented to the Patent Office, each of which assured an escape for the mis- taken corpse. This model contains a spring lock which can be worked from within. It was explained that the door is suffi- ciently heavy to overturn a shallowly dug grave. Application drawing. Patent No. 3,335.

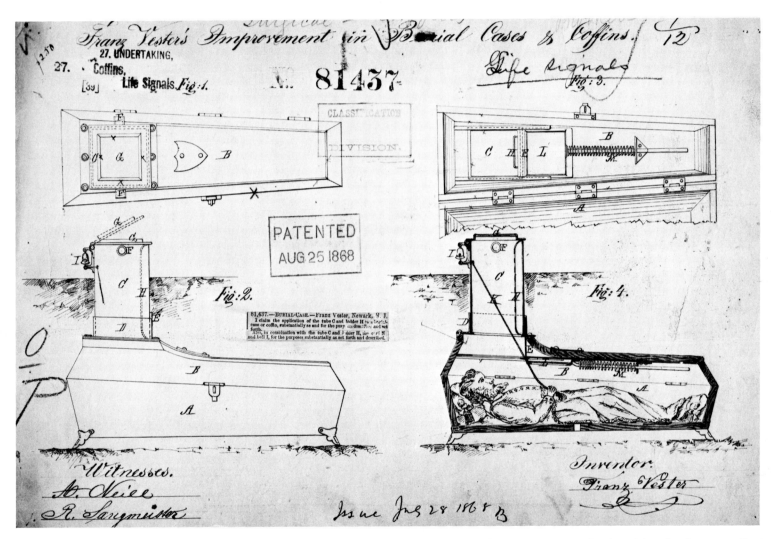

Improved Burial Case, Frank Vester, Newark, N.J., Aug. 25, 1868. This model includes an escape ladder. If, however, the victim lacked strength enough to climb out of his own grave, he could ring the bell. It was stipulated by the inventor that the ladder and bell could be removed after a reasonable time if not employed. Patent No. 81,437.

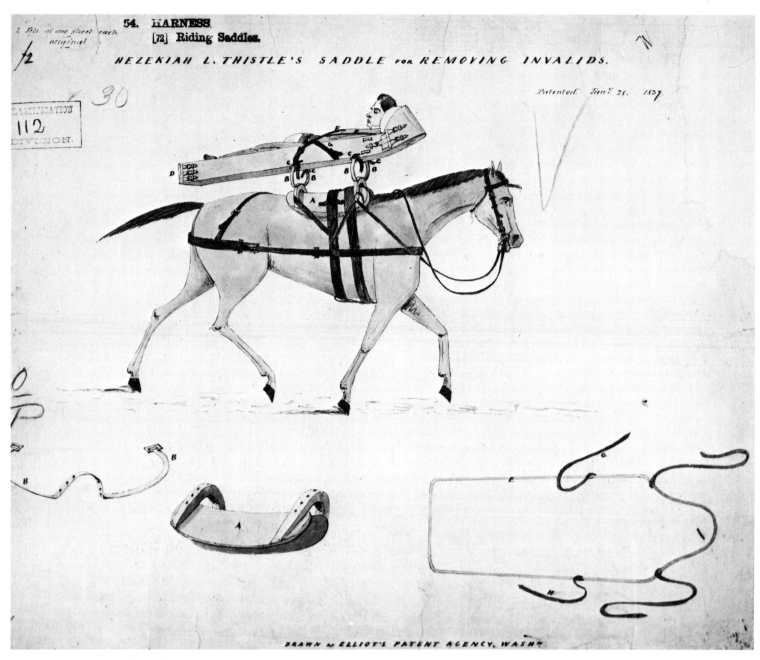

Saddle For Removing Invalids, Hezekiah L. Thistle, New Orleans, La., Jan. 21, 1837. The injured or sick could be safely or comfortably removed from home (or accident site) to a doctor while remaining securely prone on the back of a gentle and sure footed horse. The attendants would ride ahead to clear the road. It was an improvement over a jostling carriage ride. Patent application drawing. Patent No. 112.

Right, Apparatus for Obtaining Tar from Sea-Weed, William H. Ruddick, Boston, Mass., Sept. 7, 1875. "I accomplish the carbonization and distillation of sea-weed," the inventor wrote, "by means of fuel combustion passed directly through a mass of sea-weed in a grated kiln, communicating directly with a condenser. After the sea-weed is deprived of its hydrocarbons and reduced to charcoal, it may be lixiviated to obtain iodine and other matters in it." Patent No. 167,410.

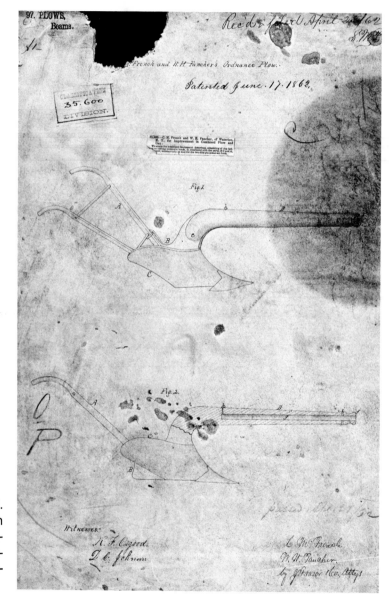

Combined Plow and Cannon, C. M. French and W. H. Fancher, Waterloo, N.Y., June 17, 1862. One of several such patents designed to aid the farmer on the frontier. The cannon does seem a bit unwieldy; presumably the intended victim of an Indian attack possessed additional means of protection. Patent No. 35,600.

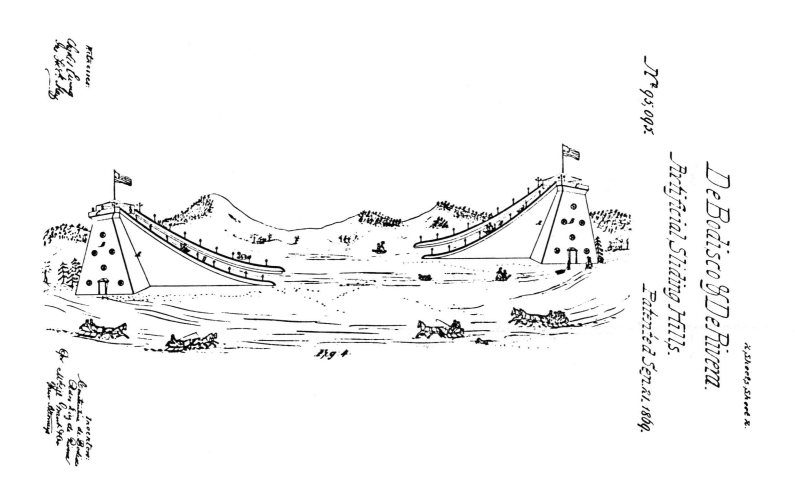

Artificial Sliding-Hill, Constantine de Bodisco, St. Petersburg, Russia, and Pedro Diez de Rivera, Madrid, Spain, Sept. 21, 1869. A new and improved method of constructing a sliding hill of wood, of any desired height, with a roofed and walled-in platform at the top. The slide is to be paved with ice and snow, and watered, to form a complete, solid and slippery surface. The tower has an elevator and a stairway to the platform. The structure was to be built on any level tract of land, opposite, but not in direct line with a second structure, so that one could slide down one, with great velocity, and arrive at the foot of the platform of the other, take the elevator up and slide down to ascend the first. Application drawing. Patent No. 95,095.

C. E. INGALLS.

Baggage Identifier for Trunks.

No. 123,703.

Patented Feb. 13, 1872.

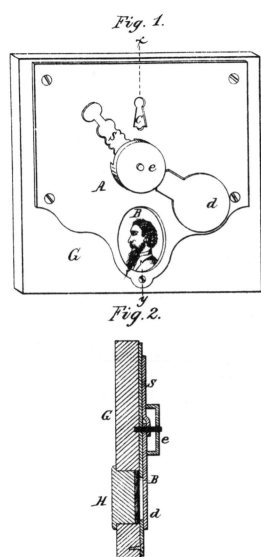

Fig. 1.

Fig. 2.

Witnesses.

Sylvenus Walker

Jos. H. Whitman

Inventor.

Chas. E. Ingalls

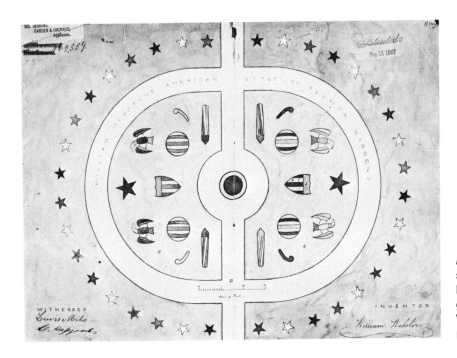

Left, Design for an American Garden, William Webster, Rochester, N.Y., Jan. 15, 1867. Webster thought his idea would suit the gardens of institutions or government offices. Every national motif was used. Watercolor application drawing by the inventor in red, white and blue. Design Patent No. 2,559.

Opposite page, Baggage Identifier for Trunks, Charles E. Ingalls, Boston, Mass., Feb. 13, 1872. A small case for carrying the owner's likeness, either a photograph or drawing, which can be inserted in the lock plate of the trunk. The picture can only be removed from the inside, and is a positive way of identifying the owner of the trunk, in case of the loss of a check or ticket. Application drawing. Patent No. 123,703.

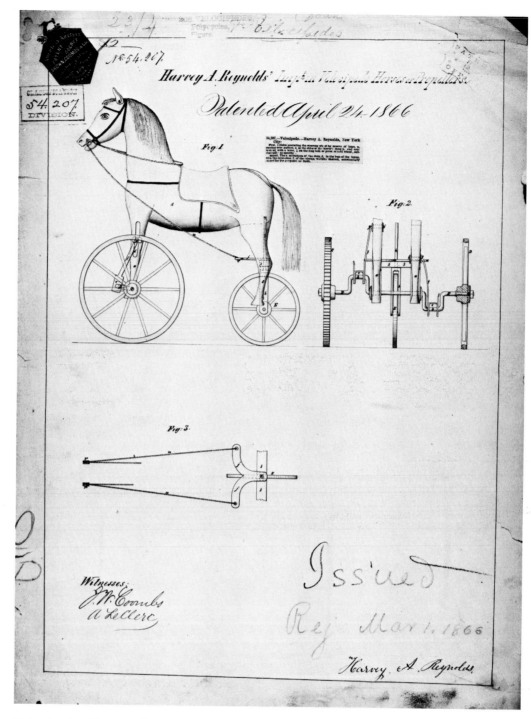

Velocipede, Harvey A. Reynolds, New York, N.Y., April 24, 1866. The forewheels are propelled by stirrups and cranks; the caster hind wheel is guided by bridle lines connected to the carriage. The steering wheel works by use of a pulley passed through the side of the horse's mouth. Watercolor application drawing. Patent No. 54,207.

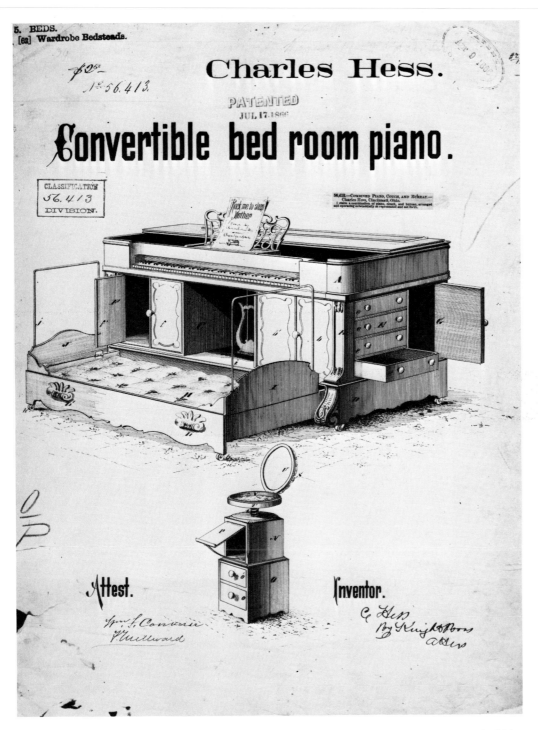

Convertible Bedroom/Piano, Charles Hess, Cincinnati, Ohio, July 17, 1866. The ultimate space saver which combines a bed, piano, sofa and chest of drawers in one piece of furniture. Apparently the only problem overlooked by the inventor was that of moving the monstrosity through the door. Patent No. 56,413.

Right, Bretzel Machine, Thomas Keller, Martin S. Keller and Christian W. Myers, Lincoln, Penn., Dec. 29, 1879. The machine will take prepared dough, press it, cut it into suitable and equal portions roll the portions into the right form, bring the ends together, and twist them. This is one description of the forming of a pretzel. Patent No. 277,573.

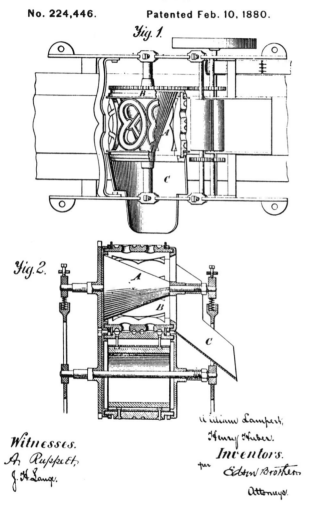

W. LAMPERT & H. HUBER.
Bretzel-Machine.

No. 224,446.   Patented Feb. 10, 1880.

Fig. 1.

Fig. 2.

Witnesses.
A. Ruppert,
J. H. Lange.

William Lampert,
Henry Huber,
Inventors.
per Edson Brothers
Attorneys.

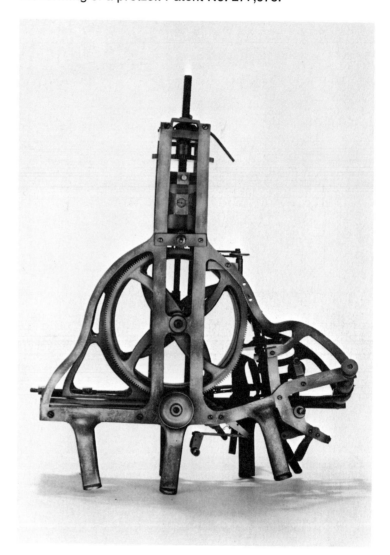

Champagne/Wine Cooler, inventor unknown. An elaborate and complicated apparatus for doing something very simple—turning the bottle for chilling.

Bibliography

Bathe, Greville and Dorothy. *Oliver Evans,* Philadelphia, 1935.

Boyd, Thomas. *Poor John Fitch,* New York, 1935.

Brown, Glenn. *The Octagon,* Washington, D.C., 1917.

Carman, W. Y. *A History of Firearms,* London, 1963.

Cooper, Grace Rogers. *The Invention of the Sewing Machine,* Washington, D.C., 1968.

de Camp, L. Sprague. *The Heroic Age of American Invention,* New York, 1961.

Giedion, Siegfried. *Mechanization Takes Command,* New York, 1970.

Goldsmith, Harry. "Abraham Lincoln, Invention and Patents."
Journal of the Patent Office Society (Jan., 1938).

Greenleaf, William. *Monopoly on Wheels, Henry Ford and the Selden Automobile Patent,* Detroit, 1961.

Herndon, William and Jesse W. Weik. *Abraham Lincoln,* New York, 1896.

Howe, Henry. *Memoirs of the Most Eminent American Mechanics,* New York, 1847.

Jerome, Chauncey. *History of the American Clock Business for the Past Sixty Years and Life of Chauncey Jerome, Written by Himself,* New Haven, Conn., 1860.

Larsen, Egon. *A History of Invention,* New York, 1967.

Mumford, Lewis. *Technics and Civilization,* New York, 1934.

Nevins, Allan. *Ford, The Times, the Man, the Company,* volume 1, New York, 1954.

Oliver, John W. *History of American Technology,* New York, 1956.

Palmer, Brooks. *The Book of American Clocks,* New York, 1971.

Parsons, William Barclay. *Robert Fulton and the Submarine,* New York, 1922.

Roberts, Kenneth D. *The Contribution of Joseph Ives to Connecticut Clock Technology, 1810–1862,* Bristol, Conn., 1970.

Rohan, Jack. *Yankee Arms Maker, The Story of Sam Colt and His Six-shot Peacemaker,* New York, 1948.

Shea, James J. *It's All in the Game, A Biography of Milton Bradley, The Man Who Taught America to Play,* New York, 1960.

United States Department of Commerce, *The Story of the United States Patent Office,* Washington, D.C., 1972.

Usher, Abbott Payson. *A History of Mechanical Inventions,* Cambridge, Mass., 1970.

Sources and Credits

All illustrations not credited are in the public domain or are the property of the authors. After the first mention, the following institutional sources are noted by use of an abbreviation: Library of Congress (LC), United States Patent Office (PO), Smithsonian Institution (SI), The National Archives (NA).

Frontispiece and pp. v. and xii.: New York Public Library.

I. p. 2, Library of Congress; p. 3, top, Architect of the Capitol; p. 3, bottom, LC; p. 4, New York Historical Society; p. 5, New York Public Library; p. 6, The National Archives; p. 7, 8, 9, 10, New York Historical Society.

II. p. 15, New York Public Library; p. 16, left and right, pp. 17, 18, 19, D. Ballauf Manufacturing Co.; p. 20, NA; p. 22, The Bettmann Archive, Inc.

III. p. 23, Henry Ford Archives, Dearborn, Mich.; p. 24, United States Patent Office; p. 25, Henry Ford Archives, Dearborn, Mich.; p. 26, top, PO; p. 26, bottom, Smithsonian Institution; p. 27, SI.

IV. p. 29, SI; pp. 30, 31, 32, Kenneth Roberts Publishing Co.

V. p. 34, Private Collection; p. 37, top and bottom, SI; p. 38, left and right, SI; p. 39, left and right, SI; p. 40, Eleutherian Mills Historical Library; p. 41, top left, O. Rundle Gilbert, top right, Private Collection, bottom right, O. Rundle Gilbert; p. 42, SI; p. 43, top, Private Collection, bottom, SI; p. 44, top, NA, bottom, O. Rundle Gilbert; p. 45, SI; p. 46, left, NA, top right, O. Rundle Gilbert, bottom right, NA; p. 47, left, Eleutherian Mills Historical Library, right, Private Collection; p. 48, top and bottom, NA; p. 49, top left and right, PO, bottom right, NA.

VI. p. 50, SI; p. 54, O. Rundle Gilbert; p. 55, SI; p. 56, top and bottom, NA; p. 57, top and bottom, SI.

VII. p. 58, SI, Air and Space Museum; p. 61, United States Naval Institute; p. 64, left, New York Public Library, right, Philip H. and A.S.W. Rosenbach Foundation Museum, p. 65, left, right and bottom, New York Public Library; p. 66, top, NA, bottom, Transportation Library, University of Michigan; p. 67, top, Transportation Library, University of Michigan; bottom, NA; p. 68, top, SI, bottom, NA; p. 69, O. Rundle Gilbert; p. 70, SI; p. 71, O. Rundle Gilbert; p. 72, SI; p. 73, SI; p. 74, SI.

VIII. p. 76, SI; p. 78, SI; p. 79, NA; p. 81, SI; pp. 82, top and bottom, SI; p. 83, top and bottom, State Historical Society of Wisconsin, McCormick Collection; p. 84, left and right, Private Collection; p. 85, left and right, SI.

IX. p. 86, SI; p. 89, left and right, SI; p. 90, NA; p. 91, NA; p. 92, SI; p. 93, SI; p. 94, left and right, SI; p. 95, SI; p. 96, left and right, SI; p. 97, SI; p. 98, left, SI, right, O. Rundle Gilbert; p. 99, PO.

X. p. 100, SI; p. 102, Private Collection; p. 103, Private Collection; p. 104, Private Collection; p. 105, Private Collection; p. 106, O. Rundle Gilbert; p. 107, SI; p. 108, Private Collection.

XI. p. 109, O. Rundle Gilbert; p. 110, NA; p. 111, NA; p. 112, NA; p. 113, NA; p. 114, NA; p. 115, O. Rundle Gilbert; p. 116, NA; p. 117, Eleutherian Mills Historical Library; p. 118, PO; p. 119, NA; p. 120, SI; p. 121, NA; p. 122, left, NA, right, O. Rundle Gilbert; p. 123, O. Rundle Gilbert.

Color Illustrations

In the order of appearance, *between pp. 20 and 21:* Horse Sewing Machine, SI; Burial Urn and Steamboat Steering Gear, SI; Lifeboat Improvement, Metal Boat and Pistol-Sword, SI; Smoke Conveyor, O. Rundle Gilbert; Sanding Device and Blow-off Valve, SI; Grade-Climbing Locomotive, SI; Selden Car, SI.

between pp. 52 and 53: Traction Engine, SI; Animal Tether and Tricycle Velocipede, SI; Self-Measuring Device, Private Collection; Lincoln Vessel, SI; Spinning Wheel, SI; Paper Collar Machine, PO; Spinning Frame, SI; Washing Machine, Private Collection; Clothespins, SI; Mermaid Sewing Machine, SI; Improved Cherrystoner, PO; Corpse Preserver, O. Rundle Gilbert; Vegetable Sorter and Flailing Machine, SI; Drying Kiln, Private Collection; Innoculation Apparatus and Dental Plate, SI; Animal Trap, O. Rundle Gilbert.

between pp. 84 and 85: Potato Digger, SI; Bullock Press and Ruggles Press, SI; Wind Engine, SI; Lamb Governor, Perry Engine and Stikker Boiler, SI; Otis Elevator and Edison Telegraph, SI.

Index